NERVOUS
TRANSMISSION

NERVOUS TRANSMISSION

By

ICHIJI TASAKI, M.D.

Central Institute for the Deaf
St. Louis, Missouri

CHARLES C THOMAS · PUBLISHER

Springfield · Illinois · U.S.A.

CHARLES C THOMAS · PUBLISHER
BANNERSTONE HOUSE
301–327 East Lawrence Avenue, Springfield, Illinois, U.S.A.

Published simultaneously in the British Commonwealth of Nations by
BLACKWELL SCIENTIFIC PUBLICATIONS, LTD., OXFORD, ENGLAND

Published simultaneously in Canada by
THE RYERSON PRESS, TORONTO

Printed in the United States of America

This book is dedicated

to

Prof. Genichi Kato

and to

Dr. Hallowell Davis

PREFACE

In the summer of 1933, when I started my research work on the nerve and muscle, as an undergraduate of the Medical Faculty, it was certainly a great horror for the assistants of the Physiological Institute, Keio University, to be given a suggestion by the director to work on isolated single nerve fibers. The technique of dissection was then rapidly improved by the effort of Dr. Z. Kaku, an ingenious Korean physiologist and surgeon, to whom I am deeply indebted for instruction in his technique. My interest at that time was concentrated mainly on the physico-mathematical aspects of the action of electric currents and narcotics upon the nerve fiber.

Much influenced by the work of Prof. G. Kato and Dr. Hallowell Davis, who with their collaborators advocated the existence of a non-decremental, uniform spread of impulse in a narcotized nerve, I approached the problem of nervous transmission by asking the question: "How is transmission along a single nerve fiber blocked by narcosis?" In 1935, I was convinced that narcotics act with extreme rapidity upon the nodes of Ranvier but not on the myelin-covered portion of the fiber. At the same time, I was very much puzzled by the fact that the rate of transmission could be reduced promptly down to 50 per cent of the normal value or still less by an application of a narcotizing solution of adequate concentration upon a single nerve fiber. Why can such a pronounced slowing of transmission velocity occur if the narcotic acts only at the nodes of Ranvier which occupy a length of about 0.02 per cent of the total length of the nerve fiber? This question remained unanswered until the end of 1938. Nevertheless, this series of work, done with an old, rusty Helmholtz pendulum combined with a pair of fine dissecting needles and published only in the Japanese language, has given me the title Doctor of Medicine.

Thus, all the experimental results described in this book have been obtained in Japan, an island next to the one where Robinson Crusoe had been secluded. The unfortunate warfare had made our cultural isolation from the rest of the world virtually complete until the summer of 1948, when Dr. Davis sent me a set of the *Annual Review of Physiology* and his reprints, for which my friends in Japan and I are very grateful. The fact that the manuscript of this book was written in a place where no foreign physiological journals were yet available can probably be a partial excuse if I have omitted some of the important literature in this field of physiology.

The problem of "subthreshold responses" has become clear to me only after I have been given, by the generous Rockefeller Foundation and the kindness of Prof. A. von Muralt in Bern, a chance to discuss the matter with Mr. A. L. Hodgkin and Mr. A. F. Huxley in Cambridge. I am deeply indepted to these English researchers for their valuable advice and criticism. I am now fully convinced that the non-linear phenomenon which they discovered on the squid giant axon (Hodgkin, Huxley and Katz; *Arch. Sc. Physiol.,* 3:129, 1949) supplies us with a basis for a deeper insight into the problem before us. For the analysis of the latency and the rate of transmission at low temperature, the consideration of the non-linear ionic currents is undoubtedly essential.

Nevertheless, the content of this book is not more than a systematic presentation of a number of action current records taken under various experimental conditions. Although the preparations I used were taken mainly from Japanese toads, it would be no use doubting that, under similar experimental conditions, preparations from European and American animals behave in a similar manner. Nerve physiology never stops its steady progress, and old theories are very frequently replaced by new ones. But the experimental facts upon which the theories are built are certainly unalterable.

Publication of this book has been made possible by the kindness of Dr. R. W. Gerard and Mr. Charles C Thomas. It is a great pleasure to me to acknowledge my sincere gratitude to them.

Ichiji Tasaki

CONTENTS

*NERVOUS
TRANSMISSION*

CHAPTER I

THE ACTION CURRENT

I. THE NERVE AND THE NERVE FIBER

When a brief pulse of an electric current is sent through one of the limb muscles of a vertebrate, for instance through the gastrocnemius of the frog, there generally ensues in the muscle a brisk contraction followed by an immediate relaxation. A similar contraction, or a twitch, of the muscle can also be evoked when the current is applied to the nerve entering the muscle, instead of applying it directly to the muscle (Fig. 1).

Although the nerve is a conductor of electricity, there is good reason to believe that the twitch brought about by application of an electric current to the nerve is not due to direct spread of electricity along the nerve to the muscle. If, for instance, the nerve is crushed with forceps or treated with a dilute cocaine solution beforehand, induction currents delivered to the nerve fail to evoke twitches in the muscle. As these procedures do not seem to utterly prevent the direct spread of electricity along the nerve, it is certain that some process which has not ordinarily been treated in the theory of electricity is brought into play in the nerve when the effect of an electric current reaches the muscle. This process is called the *nervous transmission,* without any implication as to its physico-chemical nature.

A histological examination reveals that the nerve comprises a large number of small fibers, known as the *nerve fibers,* bound with a layer of connective tissue. A nerve fiber consists of a long thread of protoplasm, called the *axis-cylinder,* enclosed in a tubing of a complex fatty substance, i.e., in the *myelin sheath,* and further covered with a very thin layer of cells like connective tissue, namely with the sheath of Schwann. The axis-cylinder runs an uninterrupted course between the central nervous system and the periphery. It is also well known that the myelin sheath is not continuous but is broken in its course at an approximately regular interval of a few millimeters. At these breaks of the myelin

3

sheath, which are called the *nodes of Ranvier* (Fig. 2), the sheath of Schwann is known to cover the nerve fiber continuously, sticking closely to the surface of the axis-cylinder (de Rényi, 1929).

It is an established fact that the nerve fiber is the ultimate functional unit which performs the nervous transmission. It is easy to demonstrate that transmission does occur even after all the fibers

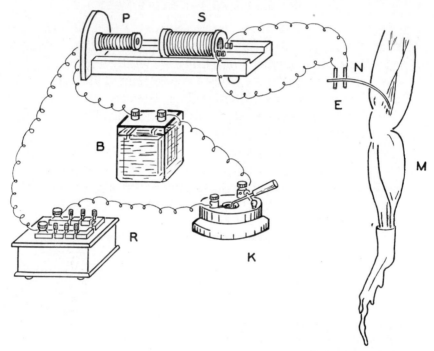

Fig. 1. Diagram of experimental set-up to evoke a twitch in frog's gastrocnemius muscle by application of an induction shock to the sciatic nerve. M, gastrocnemius mucle; N, static nerve; E, a pair of platinum electrodes; B, battery; K, key for closing and opening the circuit; R, variable resistance; P & S, primary and secondary coil of an inductorium respectively.

except just one are cut across by a micro-operation, but never occurs after the remaining one fiber is also severed. The twitch of the muscle evoked through an intact nerve is in general much more powerful than that evoked through a single nerve fiber, but this is ascribed simply to the difference in the number of units acting in the transmission. It is therefore expected that, in the investigation of the process of nervous transmission, the use of single nerve fibers, in place of whole nerve trunks, makes the experiments much simpler and more decisive.

The first successful attempt to reduce operatively the number of active nerve fibers in a nerve was made by Adrian and Bronk (1928). The technique was greatly improved by Shimizu, Kaku, Tasaki and others working under Kato (1934), and recently by von Muralt (1945) and Stämpfli (1946). The operation is now

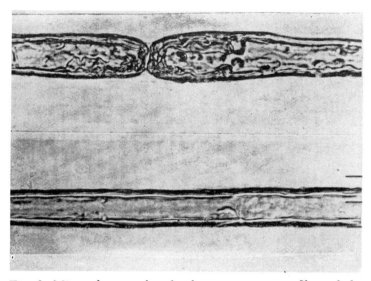

Fig. 2. Micro-photographs of a large motor nerve fiber of the cat. A node of Ranvier is shown in the upper picture. The scale on the right indicates the intervals of 10 microns. Dr. J. Nakai of the Department of Anatomy, Tokyo University, suggests that the pattern on the myelin sheath near the node in this picture might be due to the inadequacy of the ringer solution employed.

relatively easy to conduct and one can learn the technique of isolating exactly one fiber through two or three days' exercise.

Most of the experiments described in this book were carried out on single nerve fibers obtained by this technique.

2. ELECTRIC EXCITATION OF AN ISOLATED SINGLE NERVE FIBER

We shall proceed in this section to examine how or where an electric current acts upon the nerve fiber, if it is to initiate a transmission. For applying electric currents to an isolated single nerve fiber floating in a shallow pool of ringer fluid on a glass plate, the use of a so-called micro-electrode seemed at outset indispensable. Let us now take an experiment which served as the first step in our investigation into the mechanism of nerve excitation and transmission.

In this experiment, as in most of the experiments which will be stated on the following pages, large motor nerve fibers entering into the gastrocnemius muscle of the toad were used. With such

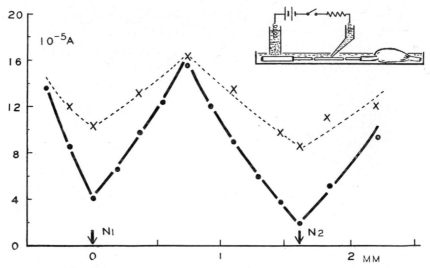

Fig. 3. Threshold strengths of long stimulating currents (in amperes) plotted against distances from a node of Ranvier N_1 of the fiber towards the neighboring node N_2 (in millimeters). Black circles show the results obtained with the cathode of the battery connected to the micro-electrode, and the crosses with currents flowing in the opposite direction. Toad's motor nerve fiber at 23°C.

preparations, one can readily observe by eye, on application of an electric current to the fiber, a distinct twitch in the muscle.

To apply electric currents to the nerve fiber, one small and one large electrode were used in this experiment (Fig. 3). The small electrode which was brought near the fiber was composed of a glass tubing of about 5 millimeters bore drawn to a point of about 0.1 millimeter in diameter. The other large electrode, which was kept far from the fiber, had an orifice of about 10 millimeters in diameter. The small electrode was kept in contact with the fiber by means of a micro-manipulator. Both of these electrodes were non-polarizable, being of the Ag-AgCl- or Zn-ZnSO₄-ringer type.

If one starts, at a definite position of the electrode, with a very weak current pulse and increases its strength step by step, one finds that the muscle responds to the current pulse with a twitch only when the strength of the current is above a certain critical value. One finds further that this critical strength of the current, or the *threshold strength*, varies remarkably as the small electrode is shifted along the fiber. The threshold depends also on the direction and the duration of the applied current pulse.

In the example of experiment furnished in Figure 3, the duration of the current pulse was about 0.5 second. The threshold strengths were determined at a number of points along the fiber. When the battery was so connected to the electrodes that the small electrode acted as the *sink* of current in the pool of ringer fluid, threshold determinations could be made with fair· accuracy. It is seen that the threshold is lowest when the small electrode is placed on one of the nodes of Ranvier and is highest when it is attached to the fiber at a point half way between two neighboring nodes. At a given position of the electrode, the threshold is higher with the source of the current placed on the fiber than with the sink of the current kept in contact with the fiber.

These experimental facts, first demonstrated by Kubo and Ono (1934), undoubtedly bring to light the significance of the myelin sheath and the nodes of Ranvier in electric excitation of the nerve fiber. Analytical treatment of these data indicated very clearly that we can interpret all these results on the assumption that the myelin sheath is an electric insulator and consequently the electric current enters and leaves the fiber only through the nodes of Ranvier (Tasaki, cf. Kato's reviews published in 1934 and 1936).

A source and a sink of electricity placed in a pool of ringer fluid cause, according to the theory of electricity, a definite distribution of current in the fluid. This in turn means that a field of potential is generated in the fluid, and the equipotential surfaces are considered to be disturbed only slightly by the presence of the thin fiber in the fluid. The difference in the potential, to which two neighboring nodes of the nerve fiber are subjected, should then generate an electric current, according to Ohm's law, which actually flows through the fiber. And, this current which enters and leaves the fiber, and not the current flowing through the surrounding medium, is actually found to be effective in initiating a process which precedes production of a twitch in the muscle.

Although this experiment illustrates very clearly the importance of the nodes of Ranvier in electric excitation of the nerve fiber, the field of potential generated by a micro-electrode in the fluid is of somewhat complicated pattern. To simplify the electric field acting on the fiber, the techniques which will be stated in the subsequent sections have been devised.

3. ELECTRIC CURRENTS DEVELOPED BY THE NERVE FIBER

Let us now introduce the operated region of a single nerve fiber preparation into a narrow groove filled with ringer fluid as shown in Figure 4, left top. If, with this arrangement, an electric current is sent through the fluid by means of a pair of electrodes dipped in the two pools on both sides, it is expected, in accordance with the theory of electricity, that the electric potential along the fiber under investigation varies appreciably only in the region of the groove. Since there is practically no potential difference along the nerve in the large pools, it is obvious from what has been stated in the preceding section that this procedure is effective in eliciting a response only from the fiber in the groove.

The strength of the current through the fluid in the groove increases, according to Ohm's law, in proportion to the voltage applied between the electrodes. If the applied voltage has a rectangular configuration, i.e., if a constant voltage is started suddenly at a definite moment and is withdrawn after a certain amount of time, the configuration of the current through the fluid is correspondingly rectangular. This can readily be demonstrated by means of cathode ray oscillograph used in conjunction with a vacuum tuble amplifier.

When the groove is made narrower, the resistance of the fluid in the groove, which is practically equal to the resistance between the two electrodes, becomes greater. This can very readily be shown by inserting the system, as shown by the diagram in Figure 4, in one of the arms of a Wheatstone bridge.

If the system composed of ringer fluid with a nerve fiber in it behaves in accordance with Ohm's law, it is expected that, after the bridge was once balanced very accurately, an increase in the voltage applied to the bridge would never result in bridge unbalance. And that this is actually the case can be demonstrated when the voltage between the electrodes is below about 20 millivolts.

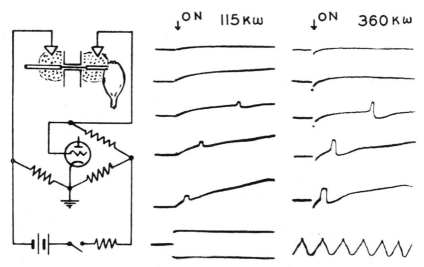

Fig. 4. Diagram of an arrangement to record electric currents developed by the nerve fiber (left) and an example of the results obtained by this method (right). The voltage between the two electrodes, generated by the bridge current starting at the moment marked by the arrows, were as follows: From right top downwards, 30, 47, 49, 60 and 80 mV; from middle top downwards, 20, 48, 50, 60 and 80 mV. Time marker shows the interval of 1 msec., and the record at the bottom in the middle column indicates the responses of the voltage recording system to rectangular pulses of ± 0.3 mV. The slight continuous bridge-unbalance during the passage of current is apparently due to polarization of the electrodes. Temperature 18°C.

In the experiment of Figure 4, the contact K in the battery circuit was closed by means of a thyratron tube at the moment marked by the arrows. The series of records on the right column was obtained when the groove filled with ringer fluid was approximately 1 millimeter long and 0.1 millimeter wide. Its depth was slightly less than 0.1 millimeter and a glass cover was placed on the groove. The bridge was accurately balanced at a low voltage and the resistance between the electrodes was found to be about 3.6×10^5 ohms. The applied voltage was increased step by step until it reached about 80 millivolts.

When the voltage between the two electrodes rose to 48 millivolts in this case, the bridge went off balance at approximately 3 milliseconds after the onset of the voltage. The time interval from the onset of the voltage to the bridge unbalance is further shown to decrease with increasing voltage. It is of great significance to note that when, and only when, there occurs bridge unbalance there is a twitch in the muscle into which the motor nerve fiber under investigation enters.

The manner in which the bridge unbalance takes place in this experiment would easily be accounted for either if the nerve fiber is assumed to produce an electric current of a definite temporal configuration in response to the applied voltage or if the electric resistance of the fiber is assumed to change in that case. Judging from the sign of the potential difference which constitutes the bridge unbalance, the change in the resistance in the second assumption should be such that the resistance would increase during the first, predominant phase of the bridge unbalance. Since, however, the presence of the very fine nerve fiber (about 10 microns in diameter) in the fluid in the groove has practically no measurable effect upon the resistance between the electrodes, the second possibility stated above is excluded and we are left with the first explanation that the nerve fiber generates an electric current in response to an applied voltage pulse.

The electric current produced by the nerve fiber, which we call the *action current*, is of a strength approximately independent of the voltage applied to the fiber to induce it. This can be seen very clearly in the oscillograph records in the figure.

We will now turn to the effect of the electric resistance of the fluid in the groove upon the strength of the action current. The oscillograph records in the middle column of the figure were obtained after the width of the groove was broadened slightly. The resistance between the two electrodes was decreased by this procedure to approximately one third of the previous value. Action currents were found to be evoked again with voltages above a definite critical, or threshold, value. And, this threshold voltage was practically equal to that observed before. But, the magnitude of the observed potential variation resulting from the action current had now decreased to one third of the value found before. This observation indicates very clearly that the observed potential variation, or the *action potential*, varies within a certain limit directly as the resistance of the fluid medium in which the nerve fiber is immersed.

According to the principle of superposition in the theory of electricity, the potential difference recorded by the amplifier system in the figure should be given by the algebraic sum of the effect of the action current and that of the current arising from the battery in the figure. The experimental fact, therefore, that the observed action potential varies directly as the resistance of the fluid medium indicates that the current produced by the nerve fiber in action is practically independent of the resistance of the medium. And, this property of the action current can easily be accounted for under the assumption that the action current is produced by an electro-motive force existing within the nerve fiber and it has to flow through a very high resistance before it reaches the fluid medium.

If the ringer fluid in the groove in Figure 4 is replaced with vaseline, or with air, it is found that the resistance between the two electrodes increases readily up to several tens of megohms. Under such circumstances, the observed action potential can be 10 millivolts or more; but in that case the observed potential does not increase directly as the resistance of the electrode system. Furthermore, the observed action potential suffers a considerable deformation under these conditions. Our potential recording system does not follow a rapid variation in the electro-motive force to which such a high resistance is connected.[*]

4. POLAR EXCITATION

It has been shown possible to imbed a short myelinated region of a nerve fiber in liquid paraffin, or even to expose it to air, with-

---

[*] It is practically impossible to reduce the capacity of the short lead wire connected with the pool of fluid on the glass plate to a value below 10^{-11} farad. If the electromotive force within the nerve fiber is to charge up this system through a series resistance of the order of 5×10^7 ohms, a time lag of the order of 5×10^{-4} second is unavoidable in the record of potential taken through the lead wire. This difficulty can partly be overcome by using an amplifier of the cathode-follower type in a proper way.

out hindering its function to perform transmission. To demonstrate this, let us take the following experiment.

A nerve fiber is isolated from a toad's nerve muscle preparation in a shallow pool of ringer solution, and the operated region of the preparation is cleaned for a length of 3 to 4 millimeters by removing pieces of connective tissue and other damaged fibers around the active one. The fiber is then laid, as shown in Figure 5, in pools of ringer fluid on a pair of glass plates. There is a gap of about one millimeter between these two glass plates, and the nerve fiber is so mounted that no node of Ranvier is found on the gap. The fluid in the gap is then carefully and completely

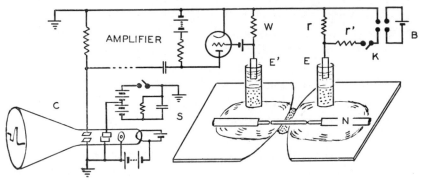

Fig. 5. Simplified diagram of the arrangement for recording action currents from a nerve fiber laid on a bridge-insulator. The fluid in the space between the two glass plates is first filled with normal ringer solution, and then it is replaced with paraffin oil. N, nerve; E and E', non-polarizable electrodes; B, battery; K, key to start the stimulating current; W, r and r', resistances; C, cathode ray oscillograph; S, sweeping apparatus.

replaced with liquid paraffin. The portion of the fiber on the gap is now surrounded by paraffin.

It is necessary in this experiment to take special care to keep all the nodes of Ranvier moist in ringer fluid. As the internodal distance, i.e., the distance between two neighboring nodes amounts, in the toad's motor nerve fiber, as a rule from 1.5 up to 3 millimeters, the procedure to mount a fiber on these glass plates (which we call the *bridge-insulator*) can be done without any serious difficulty.

In each pool in ringer fluid on the glass plates, a non-polarizable electrode (E and E' in Fig. 5) is immersed. By means of these electrodes, the two portions on both sides of the bridge-insulator are shunted with a resistance of below one megohm.

Under these experimental conditions, the nervous transmission across the region covered with liquid paraffin is always found to be maintained. Even after the portion of the nerve fiber on the gap is exposed to air, transmission through the desiccated region remains unimpaired for as long as a day or two.* The fatty substance of which the myelin sheath is composed seems to make the myelin covered region of a nerve fiber resistant to desiccation. If a node of Ranvier is included in the desiccated region, it is found that the nerve fiber suffers a progressive change.

We are now prepared to examine the effect of an applied voltage pulse upon the nerve fiber with the experimental arrangements of Figure 5. Between the two electrodes immersed in the pools of ringer on both sides of the bridge-insulator, let us connect a battery B and resistances r, r' and W as shown in the figure. As the resistance of the preparation is far greater than r or W, a potential difference of magnitude of $Br/(r + r')$ is generated between the two pools when the circuit of the battery (of the electromotive force B) in the figure is closed.

The applied, or *stimulating*, voltage is expected to cause a current through the preparation, and this current is considered to elicit an action current from the nerve fiber. Under these circumstances, the resistance W in the figure is traversed both by the stimulating and the action currents. It is therefore clear that the records of the potential difference across the resistance W give us a direct information as to the condition which the stimulating current has to satisfy if it is to induce an action current in the fiber.

Oscillograph records furnished in Figure 6 were taken from a large nerve fiber of the toad with these experimental arrangements. The battery circuit was closed by the use of a thyratron tube at the moment when the electron beam of the oscillograph arrived at a definite point on the screen. After one photograph had been taken at a certain stimulating voltage, the sign of the applied voltage was reversed and another photograph was super-

---

* It should be stressed in this connection that localized application of various chemicals (such as solutions of saponine, soap, NH_3, strong alkali or acids) to the internode readily results in block of transmission (see p. 78).

posed on the same film at the same strength of stimulus. When the stimulating current flowed upwards through the resistance W in the diagram of Figure 5, the oscillograph showed a downward deflection, and, with a current flowing in the opposite direction an upward deflection was observed.

The records in the left column of Figure 6 were taken when

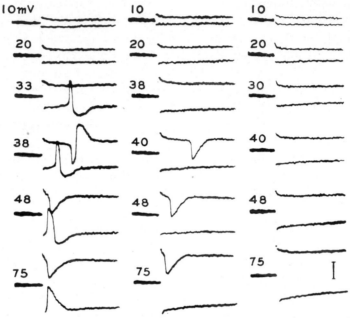

Fig. 6. Records obtained with experimental arrangement of Figure 5. Records in the left column were taken when the nerve fiber was kept in normal ringer fluid, records in the middle column when a 0.2 per cent cocaine ringer solution was filled in one of the pools, and records on the right when the two pools were filled with the cocaine solution. Stimulating voltages are given. The bar subtends 2×10^{-9} ampere, and time marks indicate the interval of 1 msec. Temperature 18°C.

the fiber was kept in normal ringer solution. The rectangular stimulating voltages caused currents of approximately rectangular configuration through the nerve fiber. The current is seen to increase, in accordance with Ohm's law, in proportion to the stimulating voltage. With stimulating currents causing downward deflections in the oscillograph, the action currents of the nerve fiber appeared at voltages higher than 33 millivolts. With currents flowing in the opposite direction, the threshold for these long rectangular voltage pulses, or the *rheobase* of the fiber, was found to be 38 millivolts.

After these records had been taken from this preparation, the fluid in the left-hand pool in the diagram was replaced with a 0.2 per cent cocaine-ringer solution. The records in the middle column were taken about 20 minutes after introduction of the cocaine solution into the left pool. With stimulating currents flowing from the normal region of the fiber towards the cocainized region (causing downward deflections in the records), it was found that there was no production of action current any more. With currents flowing in the opposite direction, however, production of the action current took place as before for stimulating voltages above the rheobase which remained almost unchanged by cocainization.

The records in the right column were obtained after introduction of the cocaine-ringer solution further into the remaining pool. It is seen that production of action current was completely suppressed by this procedure.

From these observations, we may conclude that, in the cocainized region of the nerve fiber, there is no ability to develop action currents, while this function remains unimpaired in the neighboring non-cocainized region. From this conclusion, it follows further that a stimulating current elicits an action current from the region of the nerve fiber where it tends to flow from the fiber towards the surrounding medium. In the records in the middle column, the fiber was thrown into action only when the stimulating current enters the fiber in the cocainized region and leaves in the normal region. This property of the nerve fiber related to a stimulating current is generally referred to as the *law of polar excitation*.

Another point of interest in this experiment is that under these experimental conditions the maximum strength of the action current is in general well above that of the currents sent into the fiber to elicit the action current. The third record in the left column (33mV) indicates that the stimulating current had a strength of about 6×10^{-10} ampere while the action current showed a maximum strength of about 30×10^{-10} ampere. If, in this experiment, pieces of connective tissue or other damaged fibers were remaining around the fiber under investigation, the apparent resistance of the preparation would decrease and, as the consequence, the observed rectangular deflection at the rheobasic voltage would increase its magnitude.

It should also be pointed out in this experiment that the initial surge of the action current flows always in the direction opposite to the applied stimulating current. It may be added further that we can substitute the cocaine-ringer solution in this experiment with solutions of other chemicals which are generally classed as narcotics, e.g., with a 3 per cent ethyl-urethane-ringer solution, without changing the result of the experiment. As to the configuration of the action currents observed in this experiment, we shall discuss in detail later (page 42).

5.   ACTION CURRENTS FROM A NODE OF RANVIER

Our work in this section is to demonstrate the significance of the node of Ranvier in production of the action current. We shall make mention, in the first place, of an experiment of which the arrangements are shown diagrammatically in Figure 7, left top.

Here a toad's motor nerve fiber has been isolated for length of about 5 millimeters and has now been laid on a plate with two bridge-insulators, the two portions of the fiber on the insulators being exposed to air. A node of Ranvier (N_1) located in the middle of the operated region of the preparation is introduced in the middle pool of ringer between the two gaps. The remaining nodes of Ranvier of the fiber are kept in the pools on both sides. Between the electrodes dipped in the pools are connected a stimulating circuit and a current recording device as shown in the figure, the middle (earthed) electrode being common to both the stimulating and recording circuits. With these arrangements, the current sent into the fiber by closure of the stimulating circuit does not flow directly through the recording circuit. Therefore, a stimulating voltage below rheobase brings about only a slight deflection in the oscillograph.

With all three pools filled with normal fresh ringer fluid and with the middle electrode connected to the cathode of the battery, action currents of the configuration as can be seen in the records on the left column are always observed. When, how-ever, a 0.2 per cent cocaine-ringer solution is introduced into the two lateral pools, leaving the short portion of the fiber in the middle pool filled with normal ringer, there occurs a con-siderable change in the configuration of the action currents ob-served (records in the right column), although the rheobase and

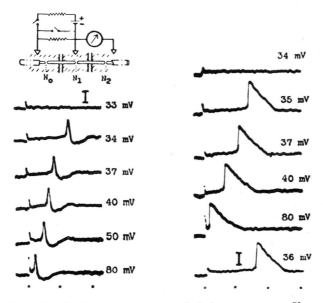

Fig. 7. Action currents recorded from a nerve fiber mounted across two bridges. Records in the left column were obtained with all three pools filled with normal fresh ringer fluid, and those on the right after introduction of a cocaine solution into two lateral pools. Temperature 22°C. (From *J. Neurophysiol.*, 11:298.)

the time from the onset of the stimulating voltage to the start of the action current remain almost unaffected.

We may now proceed to see what can be recorded if only a myelinated portion of a nerve fiber is introduced into the middle pool of ringer in the experiment just mentioned. To accomplish this, it is necessary to reduce the width of the middle pool to about 0.7 millimeter and the gap between the glass plates to about 0.2 millimeter. The procedure of mounting a nerve fiber on a plate furnished with such a set of bridge-insulators can be done without difficulty if one chooses a fiber with two nodes of Ranvier exposed near the extremities of the operated region.

In the example of experiment furnished in Figure 8, the stimulating voltage was withdrawn 0.5 millisecond after the onset. This slightly complicated the action current records obtained, as with stronger stimuli the applied current was withdrawn while the action current was still flowing. But, the configuration of the action current can be easily read off from these records by subtracting, from the time course of the observed deflection, the

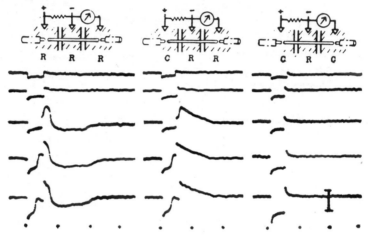

Fig. 8. Same as Figure 7, but with no node of Ranvier introduced into the middle pool. Stimulating currents were withdrawn 0.5 msec. after the onset. The bar in the right corner subtends 2.5×10^{-9} ampere. Time marks are 1 msec. apart. In the diagram at the top, R refers to a normal ringer and C to a 0.2 per cent cocaine-ringer solution. 19°C. (From *J. Neurophysiol.*, 11:297.)

stimulating current which may for simplicity be assumed to vary directly as the applied voltage.

When, with these experimental arrangements, all three pools are filled with fresh normal ringer solution (left column in the figure), it is found that action currents showing the form similar to those in the left column of the preceding figure are brought out. When the fluid in one of the lateral pools is replaced with a 0.2 per cent cocaine-ringer solution (middle column), action currents of a relatively long duration are observed only when this narcotized portion of the fiber is connected to the anode of the stimulating circuit. When the fluid in the remaining lateral pool is further replaced with the narcotic, keeping only the myelin-covered portion of the fiber in fresh ringer fluid in the middle pool, it is found that no observable action current is elicitable from this preparation, whatever the duration of the stimulating voltage may be.

Comparing the experimental results just mentioned with those shown in the preceding figure, we may conclude that the action current is developed only at the nodes of Ranvier of the fiber. When a portion of a fiber including at least one non-narcotized node of Ranvier is subjected to an electric current flowing outwards, namely, directing from the axis-cylinder towards the surrounding medium, production of an action current can take place in the fiber.

From this statement, it follows immediately that the action currents we have recorded in the experiment of Figure 7, right, must be regarded as those developed by the minimal, or elementary, portion of the fiber which is capable of developing one. Let us name this "the action current from a single node of Ranvier."

At about 20°C., the action current from a single node of a toad's motor nerve fiber reaches the maximum something like 0.05 millisecond from the start; it subsides almost linearly as time elapses and is ended abruptly after 1 millisecond or slightly more by transition into the weak, slowly varying component of the action current. The time from the start to the transition into the slow phase, or the *duration of the spike*, is known to vary considerably as the temperature; it is lengthened about 3.5 times by a fall of 10 degrees. The maximum strength of the action current, or the *spike-height*, is in general 2 to 3 $\times$ 10^{-9} ampere; it is only slightly decreased by a fall of temperature (Tasaki and Fujita, 1948).

6. THE STRENGTH-LATENCY RELATION

We have already seen in all the action current records presented above that, in excitation of a nerve fiber by a long rectangular voltage pulse, the time intervening between the start of the pulse and the appearance of the action current or the *latency*, decreases with increasing strength of the stimulus. We may plot, as in Figure 9, the strength of the voltage pulse as ordinate against the corresponding latency as abscissa. The curve obtained by connecting the observed points, which we may call the "strength-latency curve," is a smooth curve within a certain upper limit of latency.

It is known that the observed strength-latency relation fits with fair accuracy with an empirical formula which is generally

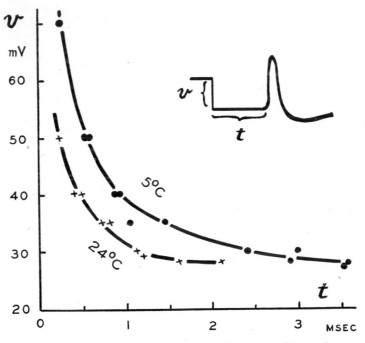

Fig. 9.   The strength-latency curves of a nerve fiber taken at two different temperatures.   (From *J. Neurophysiol., 11:*314.)

referred to as Weiss's formula, namely with a hyperbola $v = (1 + k/t)b$, where v represents the voltage applied, t the latency, k and b the constants characterizing the state of the nerve fiber. This formula expresses that, when the voltage v approaches the rheobase b, the latency t should become infinite; actually this is not the case. With a voltage of barely rheobasic strength, the action current appears after a latency of several milliseconds or fails to do so altogether.

The experimental data furnished in Figure 9 show how the strength-latency relation is affected by temperature changes. The two curves in this figure are taken from one and the same preparation at two different temperatures. It has been shown that the value of k is approximately doubled by a fall of 10 degrees, whereas the rheobase b is not appreciably changed by temperature changes.

CHAPTER II

ELECTRICAL PROPERTIES OF THE NERVE FIBER

I. THE OUTWARD-DIRECTED CURRENT
THROUGH THE NODE OF RANVIER

In the preceding chapter we have seen that a node of Ranvier of the nerve fiber is the physiological unit that is capable of developing the action current. When an electric current is applied to a short stretch of a nerve fiber including more than one node of Ranvier with the negative pole of the current source connected to this stretch, the nerve fiber is shown to develop a current having a definite temporal configuration, a configuration which is practically independent of the time course of the applied current if it is stronger than a certain threshold strength. Our work in this section is to make the conditions much clearer under which action currents are produced from a single node of Ranvier.

Let us take an experiment of which the arrangement is shown diagrammatically in the inset of Figure 10. Here a toad's nerve fiber has been isolated for a length of about 5 millimeters and been laid across two air-gap bridge-insulators. In the pool of ringer fluid in the middle, a short portion of the nerve fiber including only one node of Ranvier is immersed, and the remaining parts of the fiber are kept in the two lateral pools in which a 0.2 per cent cocaine-ringer solution is introduced in order to deprive these parts of the ability of developing action currents. The stimulating circuit connected to the three electrodes immersed in the pools is so designed that, when the battery circuit is closed, the electric potentials of the two lateral electrodes, relative to that of the middle electrode, go up to the desired values.

We shall denote the difference between the potential of the left (in the figure) electrode and that of the middle electrode by u and the potential difference between the right and the middle electrodes by v. The values of u and v are regulated, by changing the resistances in the circuit, independently of each other. And, by means of the two knock-over keys inserted in the circuit, the stimulating current can be withdrawn at any desired moment after the onset of the stimulating voltage pulse. (For a greater detail of the stimulating circuit, cf. Tasaki, 1939b.)

To observe action currents from the node of Ranvier in the middle pool, the electrode on the right of the figure is led to the grid of an amplifier-oscillograph system. The input resistance of the amplifier is approximately 10^5 ohms, and the right lower

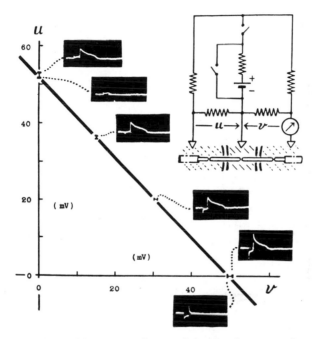

Fig. 10.   Excitation of a single node of Ranvier by tripolar arrangement. Threshold excitation by two concurrent rectangular voltage pulses of the duration of 0.5 msec. A toad's motor nerve fiber at 19°C. In the diagram are given oscillograph records with which the threshold determinations have been made.

corner of the stimulating circuit is connected with the earthed terminal of the amplifier.

If one fixes the stimulating voltage v (applied between the right and the middle electrodes) at zero, the whole experimental arrangement becomes exactly the same as that shown in Figure 7 and used in the demonstration of the action current from a single node of Ranvier. If one keeps, on the contrary, the potential difference u between the left and the middle electrodes at zero, this arrangement becomes practically the same as that of Figure 5 except just one point, that there is in the present case one more bridge-insulator to divide the fluid on the side of the stimulating circuit. It is therefore evident from the onset that either the voltage u alone or v alone is capable of eliciting action currents from the fiber. It is the purpose of this experiment to see what happens when the voltages u and v are applied to the fiber simultaneously.

In the example of the results furnished in Figure 10, the threshold strength for the voltage u alone was, at the stimulus duration of 0.5 millisecond, 53 millivolts. When the resistances in the stimulating circuit were so arranged that, during the period of stimulation, u was equal to 53 millivolts and v equal to zero, the oscillograph record shown on the top was obtained. And, when $u = 51$ and $v = 0$, the record that follows the first was taken. As the experimental conditions in this case are identical with those for the experiment of Figure 7, it is intelligible that these two records on the top resemble those in Figure 7.

When we determined the threshold strength for this preparation with the stimulating voltage v alone, keeping voltage u at zero, we found that it was between 52 and 50 millivolts. Oscillograph records obtained under these conditions (the two at the bottom in the figure) resembled, as can be expected from our findings stated in the preceding chapter, those in Figures 6 and 8.

We are now prepared to examine the threshold value for the voltage u when v is fixed at a certain finite value. When we applied a stimulus described by a set of values $u = 37$ and $v = 15$, we observed a full-sized action current, while at $u = 35$ and $v = 15$ we saw no action current at all. Similarly, we saw that a stimulus denoted by $u = 30$ and $v = 20$ was ineffective in eliciting an electrical response, while one denoted by $u = 30$ and $v = 22$ provoked a distinct action current.

On plotting these pairs of voltages u and v that barely elicited responses in this experiment on a graph paper, one may be surprised to find that all the points representing these threshold values lie on one perfectly straight line. In a good number of experiments, it has been shown that the relation between the voltages u and v that barely excite the nerve fiber under these conditions is expressed with fair accuracy by the formula

$$u + v = \text{constant,}$$

where the constant depends, for a given preparation, only on the duration of the stimulating voltage. The points representing the threshold values lie on a straight line which is symmetrical with respect to both axes. In other words, the voltage u applied between the left and middle electrodes is perfectly as effective in eliciting a response as the voltage v applied between the right and the middle electrode, and the effect of one stimulating voltage is added to that of the other when both of them are applied simultaneously.

It is obvious that a potential difference u applied between the left and middle electrodes causes a current which flows outwards, i.e., directing from the axis-cylinder toward the surrounding medium, through the surface of the nerve fiber in the middle pool. If we assume the myelin sheath to be a perfect electrical insulator, as we did in the explanation of the experiment of Figure 3 in the preceding chapter, this outward-directed current through the surface of the nerve fiber has to be localized at the node of Ranvier in the middle pool. In an entirely analogous manner, the voltage v applied between the right middle electrodes is considered to cause an outward-directed current through the node in the middle pool. The result of the experiment stated in this section can easily be understood on the assumption that it is the *outward-directed currents through the node,* and not the current flowing longitudinally through the axis-cylinder, that is effective in eliciting the action current from the node. It is evident that the strength of this current varies symmetrically with respect to the voltages u and v and that the component of current generated by the voltage u is added to that generated by v.

As it appears to us very difficult to explain the experimental result of this section on other assumptions materially different from what has been stated above, we shall stick for the time being to the assumption of a perfect insulation of the nerve fiber by the myelin sheath. The importance of the outward-directed current through the node of Ranvier in electric excitation of the nerve fiber will be repeatedly stressed in the following sections.

The law of polar excitation stated in the preceding chapter is nothing but an expression of the property of the node to be excited by an outward-directed current and not by an inward-directed current.

2. SPREAD OF CURRENT ALONG THE NERVE FIBER

The arrangement of the experiment which we are going to describe in this section (Fig. 11) is only slightly different from the one used in the experiment of the preceding section.   A nerve

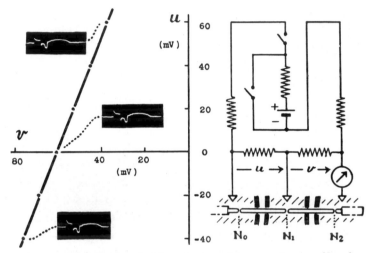

Fig. 11.   Tripolar threshold excitation of a normal nerve fiber by two concurrent voltage pulses with gradients of the same sign.   A large motor nerve fiber of the toad at 18.5°C.   Duration of pulses 0.5 msec.   Threshold values for negative u were obtained by changing the stimulating circuit into that shown in Fig. 10 and reversing the sign of the battery.

fiber of the toad is again laid across two bridge-insulators as before, but all pools on the plate are now filled with fresh normal ringer solution.   The stimulating circuit is such that, on closure of the battery circuit, the potential of the middle electrode, relative to that of the right electrode, goes up to the value denoted by v in the figure, and simultaneously the potential of the left electrode relative to that of the middle electrode rises up to the value u.

If one keeps the voltage u at zero, the arrangement in this section becomes substantially the same as that shown in Figure 5 in the preceding chapter. The presence of another bridge-insulator between the nodes N_1 and N_2 does not seem to change the state of the nerve fiber appreciably, as the fluid on both sides of this bridge-insulator is electrically short-circuited with the left and middle electrodes. Under these circumstances, it is obvious that the voltage v applied between the node N_1 and N_2 causes an outward-directed current through the node N_2. Hence, the action current elicited by the voltage v with u fixed at zero has to be regarded as deriving primarily from the node N_2 in the figure. As the ability of the node N_1 and others to develop action currents has still been preserved, the observed action current shows a quick and complex configuration. The threshold voltage for v measured with u fixed at zero was, in this preparation and at stimulus duration of 0.5 millisecond, 60 millivolts.

When the voltage u was fixed at 40 millivolts, instead of zero, it was found that the action current was now elicited by the voltage v of as low as 46 millivolts. The threshold strength for the voltage v was reduced by simultaneous application of the voltage u, and the relation between u and v which barely elicited an action current when applied concurrently was found to be expressed by the equation

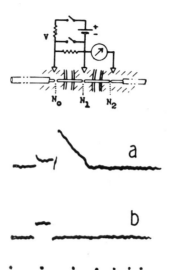

Fig. 12. a: Threshold excitation of a single node by a rectangular pulse of 60 mV. and 0.5 msec., the middle pool is filled with normal ringer and two lateral pools with 0.2 per cent cocaine-ringer solut'on. b: Rectangular current caused by a pulse of 200 mV. applied after introduction of a 2.5 per cent urethane-ringer solution into the middle pool. Time marks 1 msec. apart. Temperature 23.-5°C.

$$a\,u + v = \text{constant},$$

where a represents the constant indicating the effectiveness of the voltage u in reducing the threshold for v. In the example of experimental data furnished in Figure 11, this constant has a value

of about 1/3.   In many other experiments, it was found to show a
value between 1/3 and 1/2.

The experimental result just mentioned can easily be understood if one considers that the stimulating current has a tendency
to spread along the nerve fiber.   As we have seen before, the
voltage u applied between the left and middle electrodes causes
a current which flows through the node N_2 and then through the
amplifier-oscillograph system in the figure.   And, this current is
directing outwards through N_2.   The two oscillograph records
furnished in Figure 12 show this very clearly.

It is thus clear that the voltage u applied between the left
and middle electrodes causes a strong outward-directed current
through the middle node N_1 and a weak outward-directed current
through the distal node N_2.   The voltage v causes naturally an
inward-directed current through the node N_1 and outward-directed current of the equal strength through N_2.   When the two
voltage u and v are applied simultaneously, the current generated
by the voltage u is superposed, in accordance with the principle
of superposition in the theory of electricity, upon the current
caused by the voltage v.

Let us assume the ratio of the strength of the current caused
by the voltage u at the node N_2 to that caused by u at N_1 to be
a.   Then, the resultant current which flows through the node N_2
when the voltage u and v are applied simultaneously should be
proportional to $(v + au)$.   For threshold excitation of the node N_2,
the strength of this resultant current has to be constant regardless
of the ratio of u to v.   Thus, we have derived the observed straight
line in Figure 11 from the consideration of spread of the stimulating current along the fiber.

We shall see later that the constant a plays an important part
in the consideration of nervous transmission in an impaired region
of a nerve fiber.   We shall call this the *attenuation constant* in
current spread.

3.   STRUCTURE OF THE NERVE FIBER AS REVEALED BY ELECTRICAL MEANS

Since Hermann published toward the end of the last century
a series of papers describing the concept of "Kernleiter," the majority of investigators assume the presence of a special "Hülle," or

some sheath, surrounding a conducting core to be responsible for the property of the nerve to allow the electric current to spread along its surface. But, as a number of experiments stated up to this time have already brought out the singularity of the nodes of Ranvier in the myelinated nerve fiber, it has become necessary to introduce a significant modification in the concept of "Kernleiter" to make it compatible with actual experimental data for the nerve fiber.

Our work in this section is to show that all the experimental results stated on the foregoing pages can be explained in terms of the electrical network illustrated by the diagram in Figure 13 showing the structure of the nerve fiber as revealed by electrical means. In this diagram, the axis-cylinder of the nerve fiber, namely Hermann's core-conductor, is regarded as being perfectly insulated by the myelin sheath except at the nodes of Ranvier. The interface between the axis-cylinder and the surrounding fluid medium at the nodes is assumed to show a finite resistance to the current which traverses this interface. We are here assuming the presence of a special surface membrane, which we may call the *plasma membrane,* at this interface and are going to endow it with important physiological properties. If one assumes the resistance of this plasma membrane to be infinite, it becomes impossible to send a current into this system. If, on the contrary, one assumes it not to show any resistance to a penetrating current, one obtains a system which does not allow spread of current beyond more than one internodal segment.

In the following consideration on the property of this electrical network, we may consider all the plasma membranes at the nodes to show equal resistance r to the radial current and all the internodal stretches of the axis-cylinder to show equal resistance R to the longitudinal current. This seems justifiable, insofar as we are dealing with nerve fibers with a uniform internodal distance and uniform diameter. The resistance of the surrounding fluid medium is neglected in the diagram, as it is undoubtedly very small as compared with R or r.

By the aid of simple mathematics, one can easily calculate the strength of the current that spreads along the fiber under varying conditions. If, for instance, one replaces the plasma membrane at one of the nodes, say at N_0, in this system with a battery of the electromotive force E, as shown by the diagram in the middle of Figure 13, one finds that the current i_n through the n-th node is given by

$$i_n = \frac{1}{r} \, E \, a^n, \tag{1}$$

where a is a dimensionless quantity given by the formula

$$a = 1 + \frac{R}{2r} - \sqrt{\frac{R}{r} + \frac{R^2}{4r^2}} \tag{2}$$

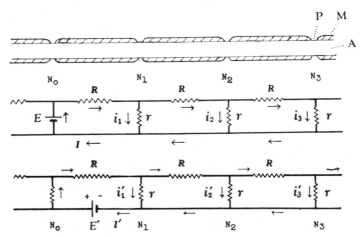

Fig. 13. Structure of the nerve fiber revealed by electrical means. The myelin sheath M is regarded as a perfect electric insulator. The resistance of the nodal plasma membrane P is represented as an ohmic resistance of r ohms, and the internodal portion of the axis-cylinder A as a resistance of R ohms. The arrows show the direction of currents which flow when the electromotive force E or E' appears in the network. For the detail, see text.

(cf., for instance, Jeans, 1933, p. 319). If, instead, one connects a battery of the electromotive force E' between the nodes N_0 and N_1, one finds that the current i_n' flowing through the n-th node is given by

$$i_n' = \frac{E'a^n}{r(1+a)} \tag{3}$$

where the factor a is again given by the expression (2) above.

Let us now compare the electrical network shown by the two diagrams in Figure 13 with the state of real nerve fiber. When just one node of Ranvier of the nerve fiber is in the *active* state, i.e., the state of developing action current, the current generated by this node flows outwards through the nodes on both sides of this active one. This fact can easily be understood on the assumption that the plasma membrane of the active node behaves like a battery. As the action current subsides as a function of time, it is necessary to assume the electromotive force of this battery as decreasing at a definite rate. Taking the situation into consideration that there exists a constant potential difference across the resting plasma membrane (see Hodgkin and Huxley, 1939 and 1945; Curtis and Cole, 1940; Huxley and Stämpfli, 1950), we must regard the electromotive force E in this diagram as expressing the temporal change in the potential difference at this nodal plasma membrane. We are concerned in this book only with currents and electromotive forces that change as the time.

It is clear that the diagram at the bottom in Figure 13 represents the distribution of the current in case where a potential source is applied across a bridge-insulator placed between N_0 and N_1.

Let us now proceed to estimate the absolute values of the resistances R and r. We have seen in the preceding section that the attenuation constant in the current spread is between 0.3 and 0.5. This indicates that the ratio R/r of the network is such that the constant a given by the equation (2) takes the above-stated value.* For

$$R/r = 0.9$$

we obtain a of approximately 0.4.

The resistance of the nerve fiber, as measured by the arrangement of Figure 5 in the preceding chapter, is known to vary to a considerable extent according to the diameter and the internodal distance of the fiber. Furthermore, it varies, as ringer fluid does, as the temperature at which the measurement is made; at high temperature, it is invariably smaller than at lower temperature. For a toad motor nerve fiber with an outside diameter of about 12

---

* As we shall see later (p. 67), the attenuation of the spreading current is partly due to leakage of current through the myelin sheath.

microns and an internodal distance of about 2 millimeters, a value of about 40 megohms at 15°C seems common.

The resistance of the nerve fiber measured in this manner corresponds to the ratio E'/I' in the diagram of Figure 13. As

$$I' = i'_1 + i'_2 + i'_3 + \cdot \cdot \cdot \cdot,$$

we find that

$$\frac{E'}{I'} = r \frac{1 - a^2}{a}$$

Introducing into this relation $a = 0.4$ and $E'/I' = 40$ megohms, we have

$$R \doteq 19 \quad \text{and} \quad r \doteq 21 \text{ (megohms)}.$$

The value of R here obtained is approximately equal to the resistance of a cylinder of ringer fluid having a diameter of about 10 microns and a length of 2 millimeters. As in the marine animal (Cole and Hodgkin, 1939), the specific resistance of the protoplasm does not seem to differ appreciably from that of the surrounding fluid medium.

We have seen toward the end of the preceding chapter that the spike-height of the action current from a single node of Ranvier amounts generally to 2 to 3×10^{-9} ampere. The action current measured by this technique corresponds to the current I in the diagram of Figure 13. Since

$$I = i_1 + i_2 + i_3 \ldots$$
$$= \frac{E a}{r(1 - a)},$$

it follows that the electromotive force E developed by the active plasma membrane reaches a value as high as 100 millivolts at the onset of activity. The value here obtained agrees roughly with that obtained for the invertebrate nerve fiber by a more direct method (Hodgkin and Huxley, 1939 and 1945; Curtis and Cole, 1940).[*] For smaller nerve fibers, of which the resistance is much

---

[*] Quite recently, Huxley and Stämpfli (1950) estimated the e.m.f. developed at the active nodal membrane to be approximately 120 millivolts. Their estimate, as well as the present one (Tasaki and Takeuchi, 1941, p. 704), is not quite free from the effect of capacitative and ohmic leakage of current through the myelin sheath. For the capacity and resistance of the myelin sheath see p. 146.

higher, the spike-height of the action current is decidedly smaller
than that of a large motor nerve fiber; this indicates that the electromotive force developed by the active plasma membrane, which
we shall call for the sake of simplicity the *action-e.m.f.*, does not
vary appreciably as a function of the diameter of the fiber.

The electrical network presented in this section may seem too
simple as compared with the structure of the real living nerve
fiber. In fact, as the result of our investigation concerning the
leakage of current through the myelin sheath, we shall introduce
a considerable modification of our picture of the nerve fiber.
But, still, this simple picture of the nerve fiber and the argument
developed in this section help to understand the behavior of the
nerve fiber in excitation and transmission.

4. TRIPOLAR EXCITATION OF A NERVE FIBER

We shall now make mention of a set of experiments, the results of which can easily be deduced from what has been stated
above. We take a nerve fiber and mount it on a glass plate with
a pair of bridge-insulators (see diagrams on the top of Fig. 14).
The ringer fluid surrounding the nerve fiber is divided by
these bridge-insulators into three pools, and in each of them an
electrode is immersed. In experiment I (on the left in the figure),
the middle pool of ringer fluid is small and no node of Ranvier
is therein introduced, just as in the experiment of Figure 8 in
the preceding chapter. The experimental conditions for the next
experiments, II, are similar to those of Figure 7; just one node of
Ranvier lies in the middle pool. In the experiment III (on the
right in the figure), the middle pool is much larger and therein
are kept two nodes of Ranvier.

The stimulating circuit used is substantially the same as that
employed in the experiments of Figures 10 and 11. By means of
two current-reversers and five variable resistors, the signs and the
strengths of the two rectangular voltage pulses u and v (see the
figure) are changed independently of each other, and the relation
between u and v is determined, which barely elicit a response in
the nerve fiber when applied concurrently.

In view of our picture of the structure of the nerve fiber stated
in the preceding section, it is easy to predict the results of these

experiments. In the experiment I, the voltage $(u - v)$ corresponds to the potential source E' in the preceding figure. The current that flows outwards through the node N_2 should therefore be given, according to Equation (3) in the preceding section, by $(u - v)a/r(1 + a)$. Thus, the equation expressing the con-

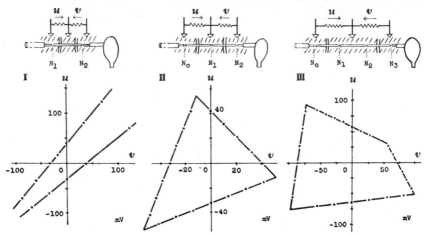

Fig. 14. Tripolar excitation of single nerve fibers of the toad under three different experimental conditions.

I: No node of Ranvier in the middle pool; the straight line on the left, up, represents the threshold condition for the node N_2 and the other straight line (right down) that for N_1; the duration of stimulating pulses was 2 msec.; temperature 23°C.

II: One node of Ranvier in the middle pool; the straight line on the right, up, corresponds to the threshold condition for the node N_1, the line on the left for N_2 and the line at the bottom for N_0; duration of pulses 5 msec. (From *Am. J. Physiol.*, 125:381.)

III: Two nodes of Ranvier in the middle pool; the straight line at the top stands for the threshold condition for N_1, the line on the right for N_2, the one at the bottom for N_0 and the one on the left for N_3; duration of pulses 0.5 msec. (From *Am. J. Physiol.*, 127:222).

stancy of the outward-directed current through the node N_2 becomes

$$u - v = S,$$

where S represents a constant which depends only upon the condition of the node and the duration of the voltage pulse. In an entirely analogous manner, the constancy of the outward-directed current through the node N_1 in threshold excitation of this node is described by

$$v - u = S.$$

Turning now to the consideration of experiment II, the condition for threshold excitation of the node N_1 has already been studied in a previous section (see Fig. 10). We know that it is expressed by the equation

$$u + v = S.$$

We have further seen in the explanation of the experiment of Figure 11 that the condition for threshold excitation of the node N_2 is expressed by

$$au - v = S.$$

From the consideration of symmetry, it follows that the condition for threshold excitation of the node N_0 should be given by

$$-u + av = S.$$

Finally, we proceed to consider the experiment III. The strength of the current generated through the node N_1 by the potential source u applied between N_0 and N_1 is given, according to Equation (3) in the preceding section, $ua/r(1 + a)$. Further, we know that the current that flows through N_1 when the potential source v is applied between N_2 and N_3 is given by $va^2/r(1 + a)$. The condition, therefore, for threshold excitation of the node N_1 by the two voltage pulses u and v applied concurrently becomes

$$\frac{ua}{r(1 + a)} + \frac{va^2}{r(1 + a)} = \text{constant},$$

or,

$$u + av = S.$$

In an analogous manner, we find the condition for threshold excitation of the node N_2 by these two voltage pulses to be given by

$$au + v = S.$$

The current which flows through the node N_3 when the voltage u is applied between N_0 and N_1 is given, according to Equation (3) stated before, by $ua^3/r(1 + a)$. Therefore, the constancy of the resultant current flowing through N_3 when u and v are applied concurrently is expressed by the formula

$$\frac{ua^3}{r(1+a)} - \frac{va}{r(1+a)} = \text{constant},$$

and consequently the condition for threshold excitation in this case becomes

$$a^2u - v = S.$$

Similarly, the condition for threshold excitation of the N_0 by u and v in this experiment becomes

$$-u + a^2v = S.$$

All the results of our consideration stated above have been verified satisfactorily by direct observations. The relation between u and v expressing threshold excitation of the fiber has really been found to lie on two to four separate straight lines corresponding to the number of the nodes situated in the immediate neighborhood of the bridge-insulators. In the examples of experiments furnished in Figure 14, twitches of the muscle, instead of action currents from the fiber, were taken as index of nerve excitation. As we have seen in the preceding chapter, production of an action current is invariably associated, under the conditions of our experiments, with a twitch in the muscle innervated by the fiber. A closer examination of the experimental data, however, reveals that there is a systematic deviation of the observed straight lines from the predicted slopes. In the experiment I, we expected two straight lines intersecting the axes at 45°. In the experiment III, our expectation was that the slope (tangent of the angle of intersection with the axis) of the straight lines extending to the third quadrant in the figure should be equal to the square of the slope of the lines arising in the first quadrant. The slight but unmistakable departure of the observed straight lines from the predicted slopes will be explained later as being due to the leakage of the current through the myelin sheath.

The principle of the method of experimentation described in this section originated with Rushton (1928) who conducted similar experiments on ordinary nerve-muscle preparations (see also Rashbass and Rushton, 1949).

CHAPTER III

SALTATORY TRANSMISSION

I. THE NERVE IMPULSE

We are now ready to introduce the main figure in the story of nervous transmission, namely, the nerve impulse, to the readers. We have seen that an electric current of above a certain critical strength sent into a nerve fiber elicits from the fiber an action current which is in general much stronger than the applied current. In threshold excitation by a long constant current pulse, the strength of the action current amounts to a value five to seven times as high as the strength of the stimulating current. Action currents flow through the plasma membrane of the neighboring resting nodes, directed outwards. From this it follows immediately that, if one of the nodes of Ranvier of a normal nerve fiber is thrown into action by a stimulating current applied from outside, the two neighboring nodes of the fiber are also brought into action by the outward-directed current generated by the active node. Then, these newly activated nodes begin to generate strong outward-directed currents through the nodes next to them. Thus, repeating this process of re-stimulation by the action current, all the nodes of the fiber are excited successively one after another. This, we think, is the process underlying the phenomenon of nervous transmission. And, when this process once spreads along a nerve fiber, we speak of transmission of a *nerve impulse*.

Considered as a sort of stimulus, the action current is of a short and queer temporal configuration, but still, there is no doubt that, under normal conditions, it is strong enough to throw the adjacent resting nodes into action in a time much shorter than the spike-duration. We know also that the action current elicited by a stimulating current applied from outside subsides by itself within one or two milliseconds by some mechanism inherent in the process of producing an action-e.m.f. Owing to this property of the action current, the current in- and outside the fiber ceases soon after the process of re-stimulation of the nodes by the action current has once swept the nerve fiber.

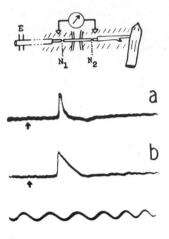

The idea that the action current might be the re-stimulating agent in the nervous transmission originated with Hermann (1899–1906). This view of electrical transmission has been discussed and strengthened by Lillie (1923, 1925), Cremer (1923, 1926), Rashevsky (1931, 1938) and by Hodgkin (1937, 1939). The possibility that the nerve impulse may jump from one node of Ranvier to another was first suggested by Lillie (1925) and has been discussed by Rashevsky (1938).

Fig. 15. a: Action current led from a single nerve fiber carrying a nerve impulse; whenever this action current was observed, the muscle innervated by this motor nerve fiber showed a twitch; the arrow indicates the moment at which an induction shock was delivered through a pair of electrodes E. b: Same as above, but after introduction of a 0.3 per cent cocaine-ringer solution into the distal pool in which the portion of the fiber including the node N_2 and the muscle lie; no twitch in the muscle was associated with production of the action current. Time marker at the bottom, 1000 cycles per sec. Temperature 26°C.

2. THE BINODAL ACTION CURRENT

The simplest way to demonstrate transmission of a nerve impulse along a nerve fiber is to record the action current which flows through the medium between two neighboring nodes of Ranvier of the fiber. To accomplish this, we may employ a single fiber preparation mounted on a bridge-insulator, together with an induction coil and a cathode ray tube used in conjunction with an amplifier, to induce and to record the impulse (Fig. 15).

According to the mechanism of nervous transmission figured out in the preceding section, the action current of a nerve fiber thus recorded should be composed of the following three phases:

(1) the phase of gradual current increase resulting from spread of the action current from the nodes remote from the site of the bridge-insulator, (2) the phase in which the node on the distal

side of the bridge-insulator (N_2 in Fig. 15) is subjected to a strong outward-directed current caused by the action-e.m.f. at the preceding node N_1, and (3) the phase in which the current arising from N_1 is opposed by the action-e.m.f. at the newly excited node N_2. In the first and second phases, the current which traverses the amplifier should be directed from the distal node N_2 towards the proximal node N_1. In the third phase, on the contrary, the current should flow in the opposite direction, as the electromotive force at the node N_1 is considered to be slightly smaller than that at N_2, due to earlier start of the activity at the first node.

All the oscillograph records obtained for normal nerve fibers (Figs. 15a and 16) indicate that the statement above is qualitatively correct. But, we find also that in the first phase stated above the strength of the observed current is far less than what is expected from the argument we have developed in connection with the electrical network in the nerve fiber. We will see later that this is due to the leakage of the quick component of the current through the myelin sheath.

If we depress, by narcosis, the excitability of the nodes on the distal side of the bridge-insulator in the experimental arrangement of Figure 15, we should expect in the third phase stated above a linearly subsiding outward-directed current through the node N_2, which runs parallel with the action-e.m.f. at the node N_1. That this is actually the case is shown by the record b in Figure 15.

Hereafter, we will frequently use the simplest experimental arrangement shown in Figure 15, top, for recording a nerve impulse. We will call the current recorded with this arrangement the *binodal* action current. The spike-height, or the maximum strength, of the binodal action current is practically equal to that of the action current developed by a single node of Ranvier.

3. THE RATE OF TRANSMISSION

When we apply an induction shock to the portion in the nerve trunk of a single fiber preparation and lead off a binodal action current with the arrangement stated in the preceding section, we notice at once that the action current appears, not immediately after delivery of the induction shock, but a considerable period after application of the shock. The time intervening between the delivery of the shock and the appearance of the action current on the oscillograph, which we may for simplicity call the *shock-response interval*, varies according to the distance from the stimulating electrodes to the bridge-insulator, and also as a function of the strength of the shock at the same transmission distance.

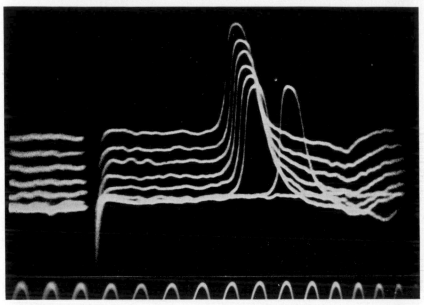

Fig. 16. Same as Figure 15a, but excited by induction shocks of varying strengths. The distance between the stimulating electrodes and the bridge-insulator was 20 mm. The strengths of the shocks, in percentage of threshold, were, from the bottom upward, 100 (two records at the bottom were taken at the same shock strength), 105, 150, 200, 250, 300 and 350, respectively. Time marker 5000 cycles per sec. Temperature 20.5°C.

In Figure 16 we see an example of the experimental results showing the dependence of the shock-response interval upon the shock-strength. In all the experiments of this type (cf. Tasaki, Ishii and Ito, 1943), it is clearly seen that, for shock-strengths slightly (about 50 per cent) above threshold, the change in the shock-response interval with changing shock-strength is very slight. But, as there is a definite tendency to show a shorter shock-response interval for stronger shocks, we have tentatively adopted the strength of twice the threshold in our comparison of the shock-response intervals measured at varying distances.

When we apply induction shocks to the nerve fiber at different distances from the bridge-insulator, we find immediately that the shock-response interval increases proportionately with increasing transmission distance. Despite the fact that the nerve fibers are slightly waving, and not quite straight, in the nerve trunk, the proportionality between the shock-response interval and the transmission distance is practically perfect. The rate of transmission calculated from this linearity is, for the toad's large motor nerve fiber at about 20°C, something around 25 meters per second. It is markedly decreased by a fall in temperature, the coefficient for the change in 10° being approximately 1.8 (Tasaki and Fujita, 1948). These figures indicate undoubtedly that, when a nerve impulse is traveling along a fiber with regular internodal distance of about 2.5 millimeters, every node of Ranvier of the fiber is thrown into action approximately 0.1 millisecond at 20°C, and about 0.2 millisecond at 9°C, after the onset of the activity at the preceding node.

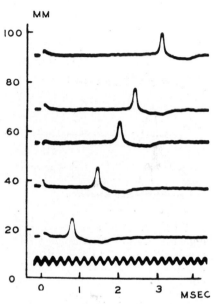

Fig. 17. Binodal action currents led at varying transmission distances. A single motor nerve fiber isolated from the sciatic-tibial nerve of the toad. Shock strength was in all cases twice the threshold. Temperature 22°C.

We have seen in Chapter I that, in excitation of a node by rectangular currents of varying strengths, the latency is determined by the strength of the current. Since we know in addition that nervous transmission is effected by electrical excitation of every node of Ranvier by the action current developed by the preceding node, the time required for transmission of an impulse from a node to the next, which we may call the internodal transmission-time, should be nothing but the latency in excitation of the

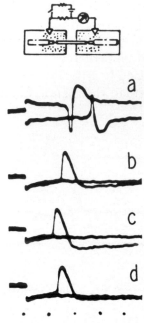

Fig. 18. Records showing the ratio of the rheobasic current to the action current of a nerve fiber. A toad's motor nerve fiber at 28°C. Record a was obtained when the fiber was in fresh normal ringer. Records b, c and d were taken two, four and six minutes, respectively, after introduction of a 5 per cent NaCl solution in one of the pools; the pool filled with normal ringer was connected to the stimulating cathode; the long negative phase of action current in record c was caused by the response of the node treated with the hypertonic solution. Time msec. (From *J. Neurophysiol.*, *13*:180.)

node by the action current. The experiments of the type of Figure 9 (p. 20) shows that a latency as short as the real internodal transmission-time is obtained only with stimulating currents of slightly above five times the rheobase. It has thus become important to compare the maximum strength of the action current with the threshold strength for a long stimulating current pulse.

4. THE SAFETY FACTOR IN TRANSMISSION

We have already compared, in Chapter I, the strength of the action current with the rheobasic strength of a rectangular stimulating current. Figure 18 gives another example of the experiments done to determine the ratio of the action current to the rheobase for the fiber. In the record a in this figure, a normal nerve fiber of the toad is excited by long rectangular current pulses of the rheobasic strength. We see in this figure that the spike-height of the observed action current is five to seven times the rheobase.

Other records in this figure were obtained after the fluid on one side of the bridge-insulator had been replaced with a 5 per cent NaCl solution. This hypertonic salt solution removed, in a relatively short time, the ability of the portion of the fiber immersed in this fluid to develop action currents, and, as the consequence, the observed action current became pure monobasic, resembling the configuration of the action current from a single node. Comparing the record d in this figure with a, we see how the node on the anodal side of the stimulating circuit is excited by the action current from the node excited directly by the stimulating current.

As we have seen already, the nerve impulse is always initiated at a node, say N_1, on the cathodal side of the stimulating circuit. The activity at this node tends to generate, through the amplifier, a current having a configuration as shown in record d in the figure. But, a fraction of a millisecond after initiation of this current, the node N_2 on the opposite side of the bridge-insulator is also brought into action by the stimulating effect of this current. Before the initiation of the activity at the node N_1, the node N_2 has been subjected to an inward-directed current of the rheobasic strength. The current generated by N_1 is strong enough to cancel this inward-directed current and further to excite the node N_2 with a very short latency.

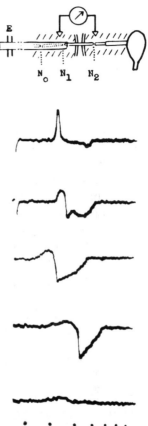

We next take a different type of experiment which gives us further direct information as to the strength of the action current as a stimulus. We have seen before that narcotics deprive the nodes of the ability to develop action currents. In the experiment of Figure 19, we make use of this property of the narcotic.

When a nerve fiber laid as usual on a bridge-insulator is excited by an induction shock applied near its end, we observe a binodal action current through the amplifier connected between the two pools on both sides of the bridge-insulator. When the fluid in the pool on the proximal side of the

Fig. 19. Effect of a 3 per cent urethane-ringer solution introduced into the proximal pool upon the action current of a motor nerve fiber of the toad. Top, normal binodal action current. From the second record downwards, 3, 7, 38 and 38.1 minutes after the onset of narcosis. Time marks, 1 msec. apart. Temperature 17°C.

bridge-insulator is then replaced with a narcotizing solution, the action-e.m.f. at the nodes N_1, N_0 and others decreases gradually, and correspondingly the first, upward deflection on the oscillograph decreases its magnitude. And, as the action-e.m.f. at the distal node N_2 remains unaffected by narcosis, the second, downward deflection becomes more and more prominent as the narcosis progresses. Finally, at the moment when the upward deflection is reduced to 1/5 to 1/7 of the original size, the component of the action current generated by the node N_2 on the distal side of the bridge-insulator disappears all of a sudden and we notice that the nervous transmission across this narcotized region of the nerve fiber is blocked just at that moment.

All these and other experiments tell us unanimously that the action current developed by every node of Ranvier of a normal nerve fiber is five to seven times as strong as what is just sufficient to make successive re-stimulation of the nodes by the action current possible. This fact is of utmost importance in the consideration of nervous transmission along an impaired nerve fiber. We shall call this ratio of the action current to the normal threshold the *safety factor* in nervous transmission.

5. TRANSMISSION ACROSS AN INEXCITABLE NODE

We have seen in Chapter II that the plasma membrane at the nodes of Ranvier and the internodal segments of the axis-cylinder are so arranged as to form, together with the surrounding fluid medium, an electrical network which makes an electric current spread along the fiber. We have then investigated the spread of stimulating currents along the fiber. In this section, we shall first examine how an action current spreads across narcotized nodes of Ranvier and then we shall test if this spreading current can excite a normal node beyond one or two completely narcotized nodes.

Let us take the experimental arrangement shown diagrammatically in Figure 20, top. Here, a large motor nerve fiber, with three nodes N_0, N_1 and N_2 exposed in the operated region of the preparation, is mounted across a pair of bridge-insulators. Between the middle and distal pools of ringer fluid is connected the low input-resistance of an amplifier-oscillograph system, and the electrode dipped in the proximal pool is connected directly with the one dipped in the middle pool. The fiber is excited by induction shocks applied near the proximal end of the nerve fiber.

With all three pools filled with normal ringer solution, an impulse starting near the proximal end of the fiber causes through the input-resistance of the amplifier a flow of action current having an ordinary binodal configuration. Soon after introduction of a narcotizing solution into the distal pool where the

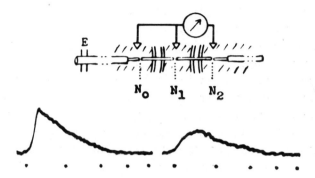

Fig. 20. Left: Action current of a nerve fiber taken when both the proximal and middle pools were filled with normal ringer solution and the distal pool with a 4 per cent urethane-ringer solution. Right: Action current of the same fiber after introduction of the narcotic further into the middle pool. Toad's motor nerve fiber at 15°C.

node N_2 in the figure is located, the observed action current becomes perfectly triangular, indicating that the current now derives mainly from the node N_1 in the middle pool (the record on the left in Fig. 20). When the fluid in the middle pool is further replaced with the narcotizing solution, the observed action current becomes immediately smooth in form and low in height (record on the right). The maximum strength of the current here observed corresponds in all cases to 1/3 to 1/2 of that of the normal action current. We shall see later that the deformation in the form of the spreading action current is due to leakage of the quick component of the current through the stray capacity along the surface of the nerve fiber. In spite of such complication, the degree of attenuation of the spreading action current agrees well with the value obtained by the use of stimulating currents.

If, with the experimental arrangement of this section, we introduce the narcotizing solution first into the middle pool, we obtain action current records as shown in the middle of Figure 21. In this figure, the record at the top was taken when the fiber was still in normal ringer fluid. The record at the bottom was obtained, as in the record on the right of Figure 20, after the portions of the fiber immersed in the middle and distal pools had been narcotized.

We are quite convinced that the action current shown in the middle of Figure 21 consists of the component caused by the node N_2 in the distal pool preceded by the component generated by the node N_0 in the proximal pool. The strength of the component of the current arising from the proximal node N_0 is well above 1/5 of the original binodal action current and is consequently above threshold for the distal node N_2. The nerve impulse has jumped across one perfectly inexcitable node of Ranvier.

Assuming the safety factor to be 5 and the attenuation constant to be 1/2, we find that the strength of the action current which has spread beyond two inexcitable nodes should still be 5/4 times as strong as the threshold for a normal node. It is therefore expected that under favorable conditions, a nerve impulse should jump beyond two inexcitable nodes. That this is actually the case has been shown in a number of cases (Tasaki, 1939c; Tasaki and Takeuchi, 1941).

It should be borne in mind in this connection that a nerve impulse never jumps beyond a *dead* region of a nerve fiber. Strong mechanical or chemical agents readily destroy the surface membrane of the nerve fiber which, under normal as well as narcotized conditions, possesses a high electrical resistance (see p. 78). As the result of such structural changes, the spread of action currents beyond the impaired region never occurs in such cases. Therefore, unless a special device is made to lead the action current beyond a dead region, the nerve impulse can never jump the dead region, however short the region may be.*

---

* For this reason, the well-known experiment of Osterhout and Hill (1930) showing jump of impulse across a killed region of a plant cell is to be compared, not with the experiment described in this section, but with the observation which will be mentioned in the next section.

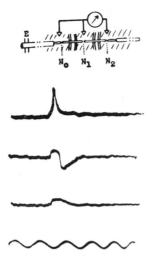

Fig. 21. Top: Action current of a motor nerve fiber of the toad taken when all three pools were filled with normal ringer. Middle: Record taken after a 0.3 per cent cocaine-ringer solution was introduced into the middle pool. Bottom: Record taken after introduction of the narcotic further into the distal pool. Time marker, 1000 cycles per sec. Temperature 21°C. The shape of the uppermost action current record is somewhat abnormal, suggesting that the response of the node N_1 was slightly poor in this case (compare this with record b in Fig. 51).

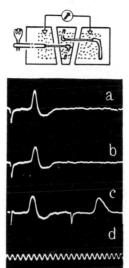

Fig. 22. Action current records showing "jump" of a nerve impulse from a nerve fiber to another fiber through rc-stimulation by action current. Record a was obtained with all three pools of fluid filled with normal ringer; spike height mounted to about 7×10^{-10} ampere. Record b was obtained about two minutes after introduction of 0.2 per cent cocaine-ringer solution into the middle pool. Record c shows the course of action current accompanying the second impulse in the primary fiber. d: 5000 cycles per sec. Temperature 26°C. (From J. Neurophysiol., 13:178.)

6. EXCITATION OF A NERVE FIBER BY ACTION CURRENT FROM ANOTHER FIBER

Far back in 1858, Matteuci demonstrated that it is possible to excite some of the motor nerve fibers in a whole nerve trunk by the electric current developed by a contracting muscle. Now, is it possible to excite some fibers in a whole nerve by the action currents from other nerve fibers? The answer to this question is decidedly "No," although there seem to be some exceptions to this statement under particular experimental conditions (cf. Kwassow and Naumenko, 1936; Rosenblueth, 1941; and others). Under ordinary experimental conditions, individual nerve fibers in a whole nerve are surrounded by an intercellular fluid medium with relatively high electric conductivity. As the consequence, action currents developed by some of the nerve fibers in the nerve flow more readily through this medium rather than through other, resting nerve fibers.

Now, by the use of bridge-insulators, it is possible, as we have seen already, to divide the fluid medium surrounding a nerve fiber into several pools insulated practically perfectly from one another. Then, it should be possible, by virtue of this technique, to lead the action current from a nerve fiber to another fiber without appreciable leakage and to bring the second fiber into action through stimulation by the action current from the first.

A series of experiments done to test this point indicated very clearly that electric excitation of a nerve fiber by action current from another fiber is actually possible. The way we arranged two single fiber preparations and the current recording device is shown diagrammatically in Figure 22. Largest motor nerve fibers in the muscle nerve entering into the toad gastrocnemius muscle were selected for the experiment. The two preparations were as a rule taken from one animal. The fluid medium surrounding the preparations was divided with a pair of bridge-insulators into three independent pools. In the middle, small pool were introduced the distal portion of the primary fiber (the one on the left in the figure) and the proximal portion of the secondary fiber (on the right). In the two lateral pools, the electrodes were immersed which were led to an amplifier with input-resistance of about 10^5 ohms. Induction shocks were delivered to the proximal stump of the primary fiber.

Under these experimental conditions, the current which is generated by the last node in the proximal portion of the primary fiber has to leave the primary fiber in the middle pool, enter the secondary fiber there, then leave the secondary fiber in the distal pool and finally, traversing the current recording device, reach the original node in the primary fiber. And, this current is expected, if it is strong enough, to bring the secondary fiber into action when it flows outwards through the surface of the fiber in the distal pool.

The record a in Figure 22 was taken when all the pools were filled with normal ringer solution and records b and c after introduction of a cocaine-ringer solution into the middle pool.

The narcotizing solution introduced into the middle pool abolishes the ability to develop action currents of the portions of the nerve fibers immersed in this pool. The fact that the observed action currents still show a diphasic configuration indicates without doubt that the distal portion of the secondary fiber has been excited by the action currents from the primary fiber in this case. If the muscle innervated by the secondary fiber was left uncut in this experiment, we should be able to observe twitches in the muscle when induction shocks were given to the primary fiber. And, that this is actually the case has been shown on a number of occasions.

It is also possible to carry out a similar experiment with one single fiber preparation. We have seen that an application of a strong cocaine solution to a region of a nerve fiber including more than two nodes of Ranvier brings about suspension of transmission across this narcotized region. If the small pool carrying the narcotizing solution is insulated from other pools in this case, it is found that the transmission across the narcotized region recovers immediately (Tasaki, 1939c; Tasaki and Takeuchi, 1941).

Recently, Huxley and Stämpfli (1949) observed block of transmission in a normal nerve fiber by raising the resistance of the medium. Although this is what is expected from the mechanism of transmission, it seems to the present author somewhat unbelievable that such a block occurs in a nerve fiber with normal safety factor. Even if the ohmic resistance of the medium is infinitely increased with a wide air-gap, it is almost impossible to reduce the capacity of the distal pool (carrying a muscle) to the proximal pool down to 4×10^{-12} F. As the resistance of the axis-cylinder is about 3×10^7 ohms, the current flows very readily for the first 0.1 msec., and this seems sufficient to make transmission possible in the normal fiber. It seems therefore probable that the block they observed is in part due to some agent which has decreased the safety factor of the fiber to some extent.

CHAPTER IV

PROPERTIES OF THE NERVE FIBER
CARRYING AN IMPULSE

I. THE ELECTRIC RESISTANCE OF THE PLASMA MEMBRANE

The majority of earlier and present-day investigators assume the plasma membrane of the nerve fiber to be a "polarizable" membrane for which Ohm's law in its simplest form does not hold. This membrane has generally been endowed with a special property that, when an electric current is sent through it, a counter-electromotive force is progressively set up and consequently the apparent resistance of the membrane varies as the time of passage of current.

In spite of this tradition, we have hitherto assumed the plasma membrane to behave in accordance with Ohm's law. The reason for our doing so is somewhat a negative one; it lies in the fact that all the previous findings conceived as indicative of "polarization" of the vertebrate nerve by the stimulating current are to be accounted for as resulting from the effect of the current upon the connective tissue sheath and other inactive parts of the nerve. The fact is well known that, when we lead the potential of a whole nerve from the site of stimulation by a rectangular current with a three-electrode arrangement, the middle electrode being common to the stimulating and potential registering circuits, we can observe, at the stimulating cathode, a gradual potential change which precedes, and appears to be responsible for, the production of the action currents (Bishop, 1929; Schmitz and Schaefer, 1934; Eichler, 1939 and others). But, in the tripolar excitation of an isolated single nerve fiber (Figs. 7 and 12), nothing comparable to that gradual potential change is encountered.

As a matter of fact, we now know the fact that the plasma membrane at the node of Ranvier behaves like a leaky condenser, just as the surface membrane of the non-myelinated nerve fiber does (see e.g. Hodgkin and Rushton, 1946). But, as the area of the nodal plasma membrane is very small, the divergence of this membrane from simple Ohm's law is considered to terminate within a fraction of a millisecond after the onset of a rectangular current pulse (see page 146).

The classical membrane hypothesis (Hermann, 1906) endows this membrane with another property, namely, "depolarization" during the activity. This may be taken as predicting a loss of electric resistance of this membrane during action. We shall now consider the state of the active membrane with special reference to its electric resistance.

In presenting the electrical circuit equivalent to the resting and active states of the nerve fiber (Fig. 13), we have already tacitly assumed that the plasma membrane behaves during activity like a battery without internal resistance. We will put this assumption

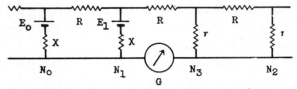

Fig. 23. Electric circuit showing the state of a nerve fiber near the active-inactive boundary. R's represent the resistance of the internodal portion of the axis-cylinder, r's the resistance of the plasma membrane at the resting nodes and X's the resistance of the active membrane.

aside for a moment and will regard the active membrane as being possessed of a resistance X. Then, the equivalent electrical network for a nerve fiber carrying a nerve impulse becomes as shown in Figure 23.

Here, the nodes N_0 and N_1 of the nerve fiber are supposed to be in the active state and the nodes N_2 and N_3 to be kept inactive, say by narcosis. Under these circumstances, the action-e.m.f. E_1 at the node N_1 naturally causes a current through the current recording device G. And, if the resistance X of the membrane can not be ignored in face of other resistances of the circuit, the electromotive force E_0 at the node N_0 is also considered to contribute its share to the galvanometer G. A simple analytical treatment of the property of this network tells us that, if $X = R = r$, the current in G caused by E_0 should be equal to approximately a half of that caused by E_1. The galvanometer G should therefore be traversed by a much stronger current when the two nodes N_0 and N_1 are in action concurrently than when the activity is restricted to N_1 alone.

If one assumes, on the contrary, the resistance X to be negligible as compared with R or r, it is evident that the electromotive force E_0 at the node N_0 brings about no detectable increase of current in the galvanometer G beyond the active node N_1. In this case, the current resulting from the activity of a single node should be of the same strength as that generated by the concurrent activity of the nodes N_1 and N_0.

Figure 24 gives an example of experiments done to test this point. Here a toad's motor nerve fiber laid across a pair of bridge-insulators was excited either by a rectangular voltage pulse applied between the nodes N_0 and N_1 or by an induction shock applied near the proximal stump of the preparation. Records a and b were obtained with the distal pool (where N_2 lay) filled with a 4.5 per cent urethane-ringer solution and the middle and the proximal pools with normal ringer fluid. Record c was taken after the narcotizing solution had been introduced further into the proximal pool and the induction shock delivered through the electrode E had been proved ineffective.

There is no doubt that the action currents recorded in the case of a and b above are those deriving from simultaneous activity at the nodes N_1 and N_0 and others. The internodal transmission-time is far shorter than the duration of the action-e.m.f. at the nodes; therefore, there is practically no

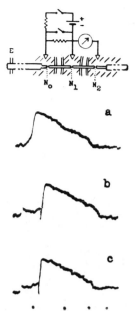

Fig. 24. Comparison of the action current accompanied by a transmitted impulse with that deriving from a single node. a: record of an impulse initiated at the nerve trunk (E) when both the proximal and middle pools were filled with normal ringer and the distal pool with urethane. b: action current induced by a rectangular pulse (60 mV and 0.5 msec.) applied to the middle node N_1 under the same circumstances as in (a). c: record of the action current from the node N_1 in normal ringer taken after narcotization of the portions of the fiber in the two lateral pools. 14°C. Time in msec. (From *Pflügers Arch.*, 244: 705.)

difference in the shape of the descending phase between the two cases a and b. The action current recorded in the case c is evidently the one which was caused by the node N_1 alone. As can clearly be seen in this figure, there is practically no difference in the maximum strengths of the action currents in these three cases.

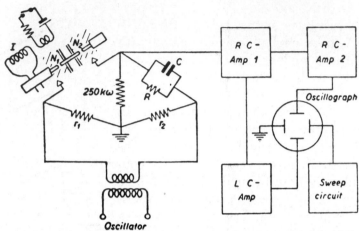

Fig. 25. Schematic diagram of the electrical equipment used for impedance determinations during activity. The nerve fiber with two nodes of Ranvier N_1 and N_2 exposed and mounted on a bridge-insulator forms the unknown arm of the Wheatstone bridge. R, r_1 and r_2 are the resistances of the order of 1 megohm, 50 ohms and 1 ohm, respectively. C is a variable condenser of the capacity of below 3×10^{-10} farad, and I the induction coil. The untuned resistance-capacity coupled amplifier and the tuned impedance amplifier are representd by RC-amp and LC-amp respectively. (From *Biochim. Biophys. Acta*, 3:485; with slight modification.)

The action current associated with an impulse transmitted along a normal fiber is proved to be of the same strength as that generated by a single node of Ranvier. One may therefore conclude on the basis of the discussion advanced above that the electric resistance of the plasma membrane of the penetrating current is, at the beginning of the activity, negligibly small as compared with the resistance of the plasma membrane at rest.

In the following section we shall make mention of an approach from another angle to the problem of the resistance changes during activity, namely, of the results obtained by the method of impedance measurement pioneered by Cole and Curtis (1939).

2. IMPEDANCE CHANGES DURING ACTIVITY

It was found possible to demonstrate the change in the electric impedance during activity of the nodal plasma membrane by the method of alternating current Wheatstone bridge. The dia-

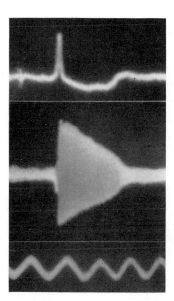

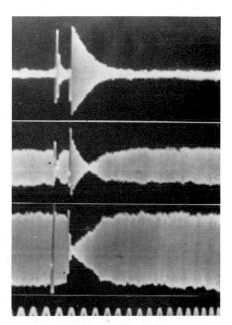

Fig. 26A. The binodal action current (top) and the impedance change during passage of an impulse across the bridge-insulator (bottom). The Wheatstone bridge was balanced for the impedance of the nerve fiber at rest, namely, 80 megohms in this case. The bridge frequency, about 2 kilocycles per sec.; temperature, about 5°C. Time marker, 250 cycles per sec.

Fig. 26B. Bridge output during the passage of an impulse, with the bridge balanced at rest or at various moments during action. With the experimental arrangements of the preceding figure, R, r_2 and C were fixed respectively at 1 megohm, 1 ohm and approximately 5×10^{-11} farad throughout. The resistance r_1 was, in the uppermost record, 44 ohms, in the middle 41 ohms and at the bottom 38 ohms. Bridge frequency 2 kilocycles per sec., temperature 5°C., time marker 250 cycles per sec. (From *Biochim. Biophys. Acta*, 3:487.)

gram illustrated in Figure 25 shows the principle of the method adopted by Tasaki and Mizuguchi (1949). Here a large motor nerve fiber of the toad was mounted on a bridge-insulator, and

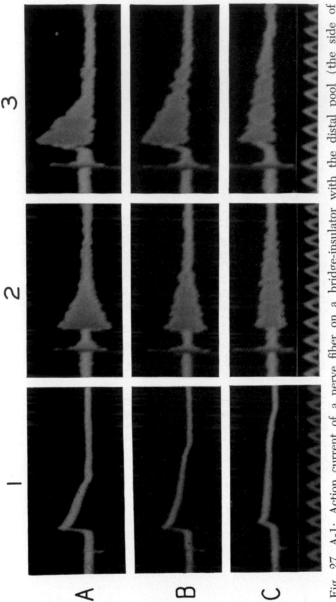

Fig. 27. A-1: Action current of a nerve fiber on a bridge-insulator with the distal pool (the side of N_2 in the diagram of Fig. 25) filled with a 0.2 per cent cocaine-ringer solution. A-2: Impedance change during activity of the fiber. A-3: Superposition of impedance change upon the action current. Records in the two lower rows, B and C, were obtained about five and 10 minutes, respectively, after introduction of a 3 per cent sinomenine-ringer solution into the proximal pool. In recording the action currents, the bridge-A.C. was not switched off. As the bridge unbalance observed was far less in this experiment than in those of Figure 26, the bridge A.C. output was amplified to a greater extent, resulting an increased noise level. Bridge frequency 3 kilocycles per sec., temperature 3°C., time marker 250 cycles per sec. (From *Biochim. Biophys. Acta*, 3:489.)

the system consisting of this preparation and the two electrodes immersed in the ringer fluid was inserted in the unknown arm of a Wheatstone bridge. As the detector of bridge unbalance was used an oscillograph in conjunction with a transformer-coupled amplifier.

When the Wheatstone bridge is accurately balanced, a sweep of the electron beam of the oscillograph gives a narrow trace on the screen. A weak induction shock applied to the nerve fiber near its proximal stump during the course of the sweep gives rise to a short oscillation of the electron beam, due to the shock artefact. When the strength of the shock is increased above threshold, the bridge begins to go off balance at the moment when the action current is expected to start. Then, as the activity comes to an end, the oscillograph line once broadened into a band narrows down gradually to the resting line again (see the records in Fig. 26A).

The resistance of the nerve fiber during activity can be measured by the following procedure: The resistances of the known arms are so altered that the bridge is no longer balanced at rest, but it becomes balanced at some definite moment during the activity (the middle and lowermost records in Fig. 26B). The resistance of the fiber at that balance moment can be read off from the resistances of the known arms of the bridge. In this manner, the resistance of the fiber has been shown to decrease during activity.

We shall now trace the relationship between the time-courses of the impedance change and the action-e.m.f. at the plasma membrane. We know that the action current taken from a fiber on a bridge-insulator with a narcotizing solution filled on its distal side runs approximately parallel with the time course of the action-e.m.f. at the node on the proximal side of the bridge-insulator (compare the records a and c in Fig. 24). We will therefore compare such an action current with the time-course of the impedance change observed under that condition.

The record A-1 in Figure 27 was taken with a resistance-capacity coupled (RC-) amplifier after the ringer fluid in the distal pool had been replaced with a 0.2 per cent cocaine-ringer solution. The configuration of the action current was typically triangular. Then, the output of the Wheatstone bridge was switched over to a transformer-coupled (LC-) amplifier which was adjusted so as to amplify selectively the bridge alternating current. Record A-2 in the figure was obtained with the LC-amplifier so adjusted that the maximum width of the band was approximately equal to the amplitude of the action current. It is seen that the time-course of the bridge-unbalance bears a close resemblance to that of the action current.

Record A-3 was obtained when the action current, amplified with the RC-amplifier, was led to one of the deflection plates of the oscillograph and the bridge-unbalance, amplified by the LC-amplifier operating simultaneously, to the other deflection plate. The fact that the lower margin of the band here observed does not show practically any departure from the base line of the oscillograph attests undoubtedly to the close proportionality between the two types of electric responses.

Records in the middle and lower rows (B and C) of Figure 27 give similar results obtained when the node of Ranvier in the proximal pool (N_1) had been poisoned with sinomenine. The falling phase of the action current was lengthened by this drug and correspondingly the time-course of the impedance change was prolonged to the same extent as the action current. The close proportionality between the action current observed and the change in the impedance of the nerve fiber leads us to believe that these two are nothing but different expressions of one and the same bioelectric process which takes place at the plasma membrane.

3. THE MEMBRANE ACTION CURRENT

According to the picture we have in mind concerning a nerve fiber carrying an impulse in a fluid medium, the electric current flowing through the medium leaves and enters the medium only at the nodes of Ranvier of the fiber. In other words, a nerve fiber carrying an impulse is considered to cause in the surrounding fluid medium a field of potential which has to be fully accounted for as being due to the presence of a finite number of sources or sinks of current in the medium. Our work in this and the next section is to figure out the field of potential surrounding a nerve fiber carrying an impulse.

We shall first examine the time-course of the current that traverses every node of Ranvier when an impulse passes along the fiber. With a nerve fiber mounted across a pair of bridge-insulators as shown in the diagram of Figure 28, one can record the current that leaves and enters the portion of the fiber in the middle pool. Here, the current registering device is connected between the middle electrode and the two lateral grounded electrodes. Insofar as we assume the myelin sheath to be a perfect insulator, the record thus obtained should give the current traversing the node N_1 in the middle pool.

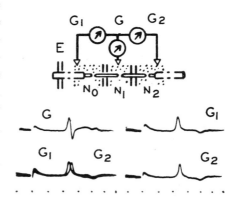

The current recorded in this manner consists of three phases, in the first phase the current being directed outwards through the node under consideration (N_1). A strong inward-directed current flows during the short second phase. In the third phase, a weak outward-directed current lasts for a considerable period.

It should be pointed out in this connection that configuration of the current here observed can be reconstructed by virtue of Kirchhoff's law, from the time-course of the ordinary binodal action current. The response recorded with the current-recording device G_1 in Figure 28 is considered to show an ordinary binodal configuration just like that recorded with G_2 in the figure. But, as there is a difference of one internodal length in the transmission-distances in these two cases, the response recorded with G_2 should lag behind that recorded with G_1 by an internodal transmission-

Fig. 28. Action currents of a nerve fiber recorded with the current registering device connected at three different positions. The record G was obtained with the middle electrode connected to the grid of an amplifier with low input resistance, the two lateral electrodes being grounded. The record G_1 was taken by leading the two distal electrodes together to the grid of the amplifier and grounding the proximal electrode. The record G_2 was secured with the two proximal electrodes grounded, leading the remaining electrode to the amplifier. Time, 0.5 msec., temperature 24°C. (From J. Neurophysiol., 13:181.)

time. In accordance with Kirchhoff's law, subtraction of the time-course of the current recorded with G_2 from that in G_1 actually gives the time-course of the current recorded with G in the middle.

Coming now back to the problem of the electric field caused by a nerve fiber, we consider the fluid medium not to contain any source of current other than those distributed along the nerve fiber. It is then evident that the sum of the current that leaves the fiber is, at any moment, equal to that entering the fiber at that moment. On the basis of the triphasic configuration of the action current shown in Figure 28G, it is also clear that, in a nerve fiber carrying an impulse, the node thrown into action latest behaves as a strong sink of current for the surrounding medium, while the nodes which follow and precede the newly excited one act as sources of current for the medium. The positions of these sources and the sink shift in the direction of the transmission of the impulse at the velocity of the impulse.

It may also be pointed out, without going into detail of the mathematics, that it follows from what has been stated in the last paragraph that the area under the curve representing the time-course of the membrane action current (Fig. 28G) should be equal to zero. In fact, this requirement is roughly fulfilled by the observed action current records.

4. ELECTRIC FIELD PRODUCED IN THE CONDUCTING MEDIUM BY A NERVE IMPULSE

It is well known that a point-source of current in a uniform conducting medium of infinite dimensions generates in the medium a field of potential which can be described by the formula

$$v = \frac{I\,S}{4\pi r} \, ,$$

where v represents the potential at a distance r from the source, I the current produced by the source and S the specific resistance of the conducting medium. The maximum strength of the current produced by a node of Ranvier is, as has been stated already, of the order of 2×10^{-9} ampere, and the specific resistance of ringer fluid is known to be about 10^2 ohm $\cdot$ cm. Introducing these numerals into the formula above, we find that the action potential in volts at a point r centimeters distant from a node

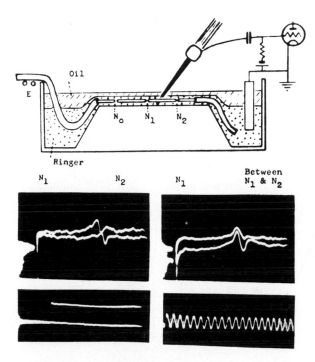

Fig. 29. Above: Diagram of a nerve fiber in a thin
layer of fluid medium on a circular glass platform,
illustrating a steel needle-electrode and a ground
electrode employed in recording action potentials
from the direct neighborhood of individual nodes.
Middle: Action potentials of the nerve fiber led
from the node N_1 (left top), from N_2 (left bottom),
from the point half-way between N_1 and N_2 (right
top) and from N_1 (right bottom). The difference
in the size of response in the left and right records
is due to the difference in the thickness of the fluid
layer on the glass platform in the two cases. The
distance from the stimulating electrode E to the
node N_0 was 45 mm. Bottom: A rectangular pulse of
0.4 mV. applied to the amplifier input and the time
marker of 5000 cycles per sec. Temperature 20°C.
(From *Biochim. Biophys. Acta,* 5:338.)

should be of the order of $2 \times 10^{-8}/r$. From this it follows that,
even at a distance of about 20 microns from a node, the potential
change observable would be about 10 microvolts or less.

If the nerve fiber is laid in a shallow layer of ringer fluid of

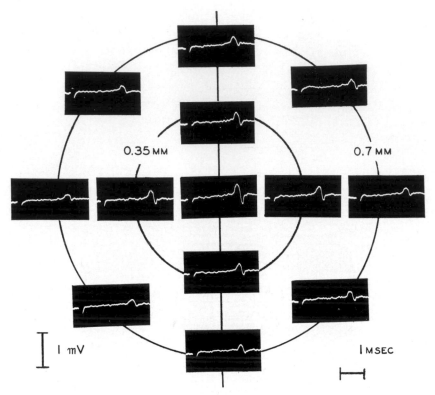

Fig. 30. Records of action potentials taken with a needle electrode placed around a node of Ranvier. The vertical line represents the nerve fiber laid in a thin layer of ringer fluid, and the center of the two concentric circles the node of Ranvier. The impulse is traveling downwards. Five records on the vertical line were taken with the needle electrode along the fiber and slightly to one side. Other nodes of Ranvier of the fiber were not exposed in the operated region of the preparation. The transmission-distance was about 45 mm., and the room temperature was 20°C. (From *Biochim. Biophys. Acta, 5:337.*)

the uniform thickness, the potential at a distance r from the source should be given by

$$v = \frac{I\,S}{2\pi D} \log \frac{R}{r},$$

D being the thickness of the conducting layer and R the distance from the source to the reference electrode. Introducing into this equation the values of I and S stated above and converting the Napierian logarithm to Briggsian system, the equation above becomes $v = (8 \times 10^{-7}/D)\cdot\log(R/r)$. It is inferred from this that, if we choose a thickness of about 80 microns and the ratio R/r to be about 10, the observed potential variation should amount up to about 200 microvolts. It is thus evident that a nerve fiber laid in a two-dimensional fluid medium should give much higher action potentials than a fiber kept in a large mass of ringer solution.

Figure 29, top, illustrates the technique employed in a recent experiment done with a view to recording action potentials from a single nerve fiber immersed in a continuous conducting fluid medium (Tasaki and Tasaki, 1950). In a Petri dish was placed a circular glass disc with a flat surface, and ringer fluid was poured into the dish until the surface of the glass disc was covered with a deep layer of fluid. Then, the single fiber preparation was brought into this pool and the operated region of the preparation was brought on the surface of the disc. Next, paraffin oil was poured into the dish to prevent evaporation of the fluid. Finally, the saline solution in the dish was drawn with a pipette step by step until only a very thin layer of ringer remained on the surface of the glass disc. Then, a steel needle sharpened to a point of about 5 microns in diameter was brought close to the fiber by means of a micro-manipulator, and this was led to the grid of an amplifier with a high input resistance, the ground electrode being immersed in the large pool of ringer fluid around the glass disc. The preparation was excited by induction shocks sent into the unoperated region of the preparation.

With a large motor nerve fiber of the toad of which just one node of Ranvier was exposed in the middle of the operated region which had a length of about 4 millimeters, it was easily demonstrated that the action potential of the fiber showed a definite maximum when the micro-electrode was brought close to the exposed node of Ranvier. Under given conditions, the magnitude of the action potential was actually determined only by the distance from the node, regardless of the direction in which the micro-electrode was shifted from the node (Fig. 30). The temporal configuration of the action potential resembled, as is expected from the consideration stated in the preceding section, that of the membrane action current which was shown to flow through a node when an impulse travels across this node.

When a preparation was used with several nodes of Ranvier exposed in the operated region, as shown by the diagram of Figure 29, it was immediately found that the action potentials led from different nodes of the fiber attained their maxima at different times after the delivery of the shock. The difference in the times to the maxima was actually in good agreement with what was expected from the rate of transmission of the impulse. It was

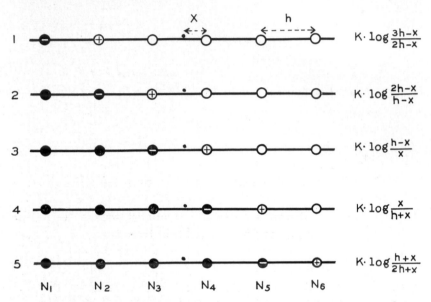

Fig. 31. Diagram illustrating shift of the sources and sinks of current during transmission of an impulse along a nerve fiber. The white circles represent the resting nodes and black circles the nodes in action, each straight line indicating one state of the nerve fiber. For the mathematical expressions, see text.

further shown that, with the micro-electrode placed along the fiber at the point half-way between two neighboring nodes, small and slow action potential records are obtained. All the action potential records taken under these circumstances show an unmistakably slower rising phase than those taken directly from a single node electrically insulated with bridge-insulators from the remaining nodes.

Let us now consider how these slow action potentials are to be interpreted. The diagram of Figure 31 is constructed to show the conditions of the nerve fiber near the micro-electrode when an impulse travels across this region. The empty circles in this figure represent the resting nodes of the fiber and the solid circles the nodes in action. If the fiber is in the state labeled "1" in the figure, the node N_1 acts as a strong sink and N_2 as a strong source of electric current. Further, judging from the time-course of the record G in Figure 28, node N_3 and about 20 nodes on the left-hand side of N_1 are considered to behave as weak sources. At room temperature, the whole duration of the action-e.m.f. (spike) is approximately 20 times as long as the internodal transmission-time; this ratio becomes greater at lower temperature, as the Q_{10} value for the spike-duration is 3.5 while that for the rate of transmission is about 1.8 (Tasaki and Fujita, 1948).

Let us assume for the sake of simplicity that all these nodes are in a shallow layer of ringer fluid of a constant thickness. Then, by virtue of the theory of potential, we should be able to roughly estimate the potential caused by these sources and sinks in the conducting layer. Let us denote the internodal distance, which is assumed to be constant all over, by h and the distance from the node N_4 to the micro-electrode by x. In the state "1" in Figure 31, the distance from the strongest source N_2 to the micro-electrode is equal to $2h - x$ and that from the strongest sink N_1 is given by $3h - x$. If, therefore, we neglect the effect of the weak sources remote from the active-inactive boundary, the potential at the site of the micro-electrode is considered to be given by $(IS/2\pi D) \cdot \log\{(3h - x)/(2h - x)\}$. This formula is given on the right-hand side of the figure, where the constant $(IS/2\pi D)$ is replaced by K.

As the impulse progresses, the active-inactive boundary shifts in the direction of transmission, namely, rightwards in the figure. This naturally changes the distances from the micro-electrode to the source and the sink, causing a change in the potential at the site of the electrode. Thus, it is expected that, as the impulse jumps from node to node, the potential of the micro-electrode varies according to the series given on the right-hand side of the figure.

In the case where the micro-electrode is placed at the point half-way between two neighboring nodes, namely, $x = h/2$, this series becomes

$$\ldots, \quad \log \frac{5}{3}, \quad \log \frac{3}{1}, \quad \log \frac{1}{1}, \quad \log \frac{1}{3}, \quad \log \frac{3}{5}, \quad \ldots$$

multiplied by the constant K. If, on the contrary, the micro-electrode is place in the direct neighborhood of one of the nodes, we may take the value of x as being approximately equal to the thickness D of the conducting layer. Then, the series expressing the temporal change in the potential becomes

$$\ldots, \quad \log \frac{3}{2}, \quad \log \frac{2}{1}, \quad \log \frac{h}{D}, \quad \log \frac{D}{h}, \quad \log \frac{1}{2}, \quad \log \frac{2}{3}, \quad \ldots$$

Although our neglect of the weak sources along the fiber, and also of the leakage of the current through the myelin sheath, is expected to limit the accuracy of our argument, we may safely conclude that the slow action potential which we have recorded is the one which is caused by the field of potential figured out above.

In 1940, Pfaffmann recorded action potentials from an isolated nerve fiber suspended in oil and obtained greater responses at the nodes of Ranvier than at the internodal regions. We believe the conditions of his experiment to be, unlike those of the experiment stated in this section, similar to those of previous experiments with nerve trunks. For the reason which will be described in the last chapter of this book, the variation in the magnitude of action-potential along the nerve fiber is, under the conditions of his experiment, expected to be extremely small. Probably the input-resistance of his amplifier was not high enough as compared with the resistance of the fiber, thus resulting in a marked variation in the spike-height.

CHAPTER V

THE MYELIN SHEATH

I. ACTION CURRENTS LED THROUGH THE MYELIN SHEATH

We now come to the problem of the leakage of electric current through the myelin sheath which we have neglected in all our considerations of nervous transmission stated up to this time. Leakage of the action current through the myelin sheath can readily be demonstrated by the experimental arrangement shown diagrammatically in Figure 32, top. Here, a single fiber preparation with two nodes of Ranvier exposed in the operated region is laid across two sets of bridge-insulators. As in the experiment of Figure 8 in Chapter I, the width of the small pool in the middle is about 1 millimeter or slightly more and the length of each of the regions on the bridge-insulator is about 0.15 millimeter. Two nodes of Ranvier of the preparation are kept in the lateral large pools, and in the middle is immersed the myelinated portion of the fiber. Electrodes dipped in the lateral pools are grounded and the one immersed in the middle pool is led to the grid of an amplifier with low input-resistance.

When an impulse is initiated in this fiber by application of an induction shock at a site remote from the operated region of the fiber, a brief current directed outwards through the myelinated portion of the fiber is seen to traverse the amplifier. Records of such action currents show two clearly defined peaks at an interval of about 0.1 millisecond which undoubtedly correspond to the internodal transmission-time. The maximum strength of this action current is, as can be seen in the example furnished in Figure 33, approximately one half of the maximum of the normal binodal action current of the fiber.

Of these two peaks in the action current led through the myelin sheath, the first peak starts at the moment when the proximal node N_1 is considered to be brought in action. We have seen already that the ascending limb of the binodal action current is indicative of the start of the action-e.m.f. at the proximal node N_1.

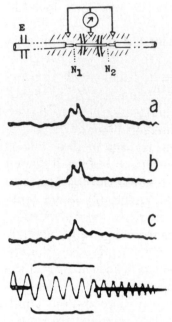

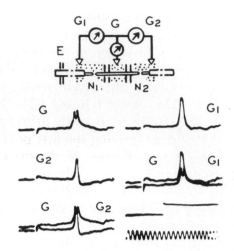

Fig. 32. Records of action currents led through the myelin sheath. a: Record obtained with the three pools filled with normal ringer. b: Record taken after replacing the fluid in the middle pool with a 0.1 per cent cocaine-ringer solution. c: Record observed after introduction of the same narcotizing solution into the distal pool. Bottom: A rectangular current pulse of $\pm 10^{-9}$ ampere sent through the input of the amplifier, and the time marker of 5000 cycles per sec. 16°C. (From *Pflügers Arch.*, 245:769.)

Fig. 33. Action currents of a nerve fiber taken with the current register-ing circuit connected at three different positions. The portion of the nerve fiber in the middle pool was 1.1 mm. in length and no node of Ranvier was therein immersed. The width of the gaps between the pools was 0.15 mm. The distance from the stimulating electrodes E to the node N_1 was 45 mm., and the distance between N_1 and N_2 was 2.05 mm. Temperature 21°C. Calibration 2×10^{-9} ampere; time marker, 5000 cycles per sec. (From *Biochim. Biophys. Acta*, 5:341.)

And, as is clearly shown in Figure 33, the start of the first peak is nearly synchronous with the start of the binodal action current. It is also shown in Figure 33 that the second peak in the action current led through the myelin sheath is practically synchronous with the descending limb of the binodal action current. This is a clear indication that the start of the second peak is induced by the start of the action-e.m.f. at the distal node N_2.

The configuration of the action current led through the myelin sheath is scarcely affected by application of a dilute cocaine solution upon the myelin-covered portion from which the current is led (record b in Fig. 32). Narcotization of the distal node N_2 is effective to instantly extinguish the second peak in the action current, leaving the first peak unaffected (record c).

After narcotization of the distal node N_2, the action-e.m.f. at the node N_1 causes through N_2 a current which lasts as long as 1 to 2 milliseconds. The fact that the current led through the myelin sheath at this stage shows an extremely quick subsidence is undoubtedly a direct indication of the reactive, or capacitative, property of the myelin sheath. A constant voltage applied across this myelin-covered portion of the nerve fiber is expected to cause through this sheath a current which decays approximately exponentially with a very short time-constant.

The fact that the myelin sheath is reactive is of utmost importance in the theory of electrical excitation of the nerve fiber and, in consequence, in the consideration of the mechanism of nervous transmission. Suppose that the plasma membrane of one of the nodes of Ranvier of a resting nerve fiber is, at an instant, suddenly thrown into action by some agent. Then, if the myelin sheath were composed of perfect insulator, or at least of material with high specific ohmic resistance, the neighboring nodes should immediately be traversed by an outward-directed current at that moment. But, the myelin sheath behaves, in reality, like a leaky condenser, and not purely ohmic. It is therefore evident that a certain finite amount of time is required for the current to spread along the fiber and reach the neighboring node (cf. Tasaki, 1950c). Bogue and Rosenberg (1935) have shown a similar phenomenon on the whole nerve trunk. And this finite speed of spread of the potential wave along the myelin sheath is considered to be the main factor determining the latency in excitation of a node by the action-e.m.f. at the neighboring node. For a rigorous quantitative argument of this phenomenon, however, a tedious mathematical analysis is required. We shall reserve such an argument to a subsequent monograph dealing with the theory of nerve excitation.

2. THE METHOD OF THRESHOLD REDUCTION

Although the method of leading off action currents through the myelin sheath has provided us with considerable direct information relative to the electrical properties of the myelin sheath, it seems worthy of mention in this place about a series of experiments which employed an entirely different method and have served to clarify some aspects of the behavior of the myelin sheath. Here, we may digress for a moment to describe the principle of the method which we may call the method of threshold reduction.

If one applies induction shocks of varying strengths to the op-

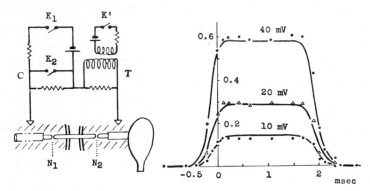

Fig. 34. Curve of threshold changes induced by rectangular voltage pulses of three different strengths. The conditioning pulses, generated by the circuit C in the diagram, was started at the time zero and withdrawn at 2 msec. Temperature 20°C. (From *Pflügers Arch.*, 244:127.)

erated region of a single fiber preparation (Fig. 34, top), one can determine the threshold strength for the fiber at an accuracy of about 2 per cent. Whether we take the action current of the fiber as index or we take muscular contractions instead, does not affect the result at all. During passage of a subthreshold rectangular current pulse through the same portion of the fiber, the threshold for induction shocks is known to show a value different from that in the unconditioned state of the fiber.

We may denote the threshold strength of the fiber determined by applying induction shocks without accompaniment of the subthreshold (or conditioning) pulse by S_0, and the threshold value

modified by the conditioning pulse by S. Then, the difference between these two values $(S_0 - S)$ is expected to depend upon both
the strength of the conditioning pulse and the time-interval from
the start of the conditioning pulse to the moment at which the induction (or testing) shock is delivered.

The three curves furnished in Figure 34 show the change in
the threshold for test shock caused by rectangular pulses of three
different voltages. In this diagram, the values of $(S_0 - S)/S_0$ are
plotted as ordinate against the time from the start of the rectangular pulse as abscissa. We see

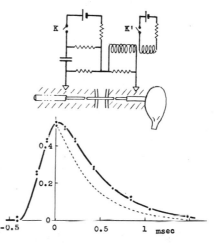

in this diagram that there is
no change in the threshold for
the test shock in the time
longer than about 0.5 millisecond before the start and
longer than about 0.3 millisecond after the end of the
conditioning rectangular pulse.
During the period between
these two limits, the value
$(S_0 - S)/S_0$, which we may
call the *threshold reduction*,
shows variations which can be
expressed by curves having
blurred, but roughly rectangular configurations. At any
given time, the threshold depression varies directly as the
strength of the rectangular
voltage, provided that the

Fig. 35. Curve of threshold changes
induced by a condenser shock of the
time-constant of 0.5 msec. The time-
course of the conditioning shock is
given by the broken line. Temperature 20°C. (From *Pflügers Arch.*,
244:127.)

conditioning pulse is not so strong as to make the threshold reduction exceed about 0.6.

If we employ, as a conditioning pulse, an exponentially subsiding voltage in place of a rectangular voltage pulse, we obtain
a threshold reduction curve with a roughly exponential configuration (Fig. 35). It is found that, in all cases, the time-course
of the threshold reduction portrays, though suffering a definite
deformation, the course of the applied voltage in quantitative
manner.

We may utilize the result of these experiments, without going into detail of the discussion concerning the mechanism of threshold variation by a conditioning pulse, in an attempt to explore the time-course of some unknown subthreshold stimulating current. When a subthreshold current of an unknown temporal configuration is acting on a nerve fiber, it should be possible to figure out its time-course by measuring the threshold reduction caused by this current. The curve expressing the time-course of the threshold reduction can therefore be compared to the deflection of a galvanometer with inertia.

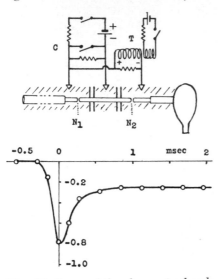

Mathematically speaking, the relation between the time-course of a subthreshold conditioning shock and the resulting threshold reduction is one which can be expressed in terms of a simple integral equation, although its actual solution may in any given case be beyond our reach (see Tasaki, 1942 and 1950b).

Fig. 36. Curve of the change in threshold of a nerve fiber produced by a constant voltage of 180 mV applied to the myelin-covered portion of the fiber. Temperature 16°C. (From Maruyama, 1942.)

The experimental basis for the method described in this section was first laid by Hodgkin (1937) when he succeeded in mapping out the parallelism between the time-course of the electrical response and that of the threshold variation beyond a region of nerve where the transmission was blocked by compression.

3. THE CURRENT GENERATED BY A CONSTANT VOLTAGE THROUGH THE MYELIN SHEATH

The time-course of the current which a constant voltage causes to flow through the myelin sheath can be mapped out by the following procedure. With the experimental set-up of Figure 36, top, the two lateral pools are connected to the anode of the conditioning circuit, the middle small pool being connected to the cathode. When the conditioning circuit is closed, a current tends to enter the fiber through both N_1 and N_2 and to exit through the myelin-covered portion in the middle pool. If, therefore, the myelin sheath were a perfect electrical insulator, then the conditioning voltage would cause no current through the nerve fiber and consequently the threshold for the test shock would not be influenced by the conditioning pulse. If the myelin sheath were leaky, both N_1 and N_2 would be traversed by an inward-directed current and there would be a corresponding change in the threshold strength for the test shock. The result of actual threshold measurements indicated that, following make of the conditioning circuit, there is, at both N_1 and N_2, a threshold change as illustrated in Figure 36, bottom.

The time-course of threshold changes by a current sent through the myelin sheath has been the object of repeated studies by Maruyama, working at my suggestion. He pointed out a slight mistake in a previous report (Tasaki, 1940, Fig. 8B) and applied the method for the study of the effects of various chemicals on the myelin sheath.

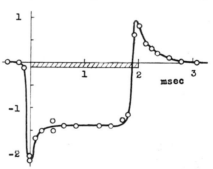

According to the results of all those threshold measurements, the current which traverses the myelin sheath when a constant voltage is applied to the fiber resembles, in its time-course, the current through a leaky condenser connected with a battery

Fig. 37. Curve of the threshold change induced by a rectangular pulse of 400 mV and 2 msec. applied to the myelin-covered portion of a nerve fiber. The arrangement shown in the preceding figure was employed. Temperature 20°C.

through a resistance. The initial peak in this current is considered to be far higher than that of the threshold reduction curve in Figure 36, because brief current pulses are known to be less effective in changing threshold than a constant current. For the study of this initial peak, the method of threshold reduction is undoubtedly less relevant than the method of recording leakage of action current through the myelin sheath with an oscillograph.

If the initial peak stated above is due to a counter-e.m.f. resulting from passage of current through the myelin sheath, it should be possible to observe, on removal of the imposed voltage, a current flowing in the opposite direction for a brief period. Figure 37 shows that this is actually the case. It is seen in this figure that, immediately following withdrawal of the conditioning voltage, there is a marked reversal in the threshold change for the test shock. In case the middle pool is connected to the cathode of the conditioning circuit, the change in the threshold is such that there occurs a pronounced threshold reduction following break of the conditioning circuit. In the example furnished in Figure 37, the threshold reduction actually amounts to almost 1. This means, by definition of threshold reduction, an impulse is elicitable at this stage by an extremely weak test shock. Since the threshold reduction increases with increasing strength of the conditioning pulse, it follows that a conditioning pulse of a strength slightly above that used in this experiment should elicit an impulse by itself on its withdrawal. And, that this actually occurs has been shown by this and other types of experiments.

In electric stimulation of a whole nerve, it is well known that an anodal current excites the nerve on its withdrawal. If the electrode placed on the nerve trunk is relatively small in size, a situation similar to that in the experiment of Figure 37 is expected to occur very frequently. It is thus evident that the break excitation at anode is to be attributed mainly to this property of the myelin sheath. The connective tissue sheath which covers the nerve trunk is also considered to provide a condition favorable for break excitation in nerve. In an isolated single nerve fiber mounted on a wide bridge-insulator, break excitation at anode is not observable in general.

4. THE EFFECTS OF NARCOTICS AND ELECTROLYTES UPON THE MYELIN SHEATH

Applying various chemicals upon the myelin-covered portion of the nerve fiber, Maruyama discovered that the ohmic resistance of the myelin sheath is pronouncedly affected by narcotics and electrolytes. The upper diagram in Figure 38 shows a typical example of his experiments on the effect of urethane upon the myelin sheath. Employing the experimental set-up shown in Figure

36, top, and with all three pools filled with normal ringer fluid, the threshold reduction curve shown by the continuous line in the figure was obtained. After replacing the fluid in the middle pool with a 5 per cent urethane-ringer solution, the curve given by the broken line was secured.

As has been stated in the preceding section, the current generated by a constant voltage through the myelin sheath is made up

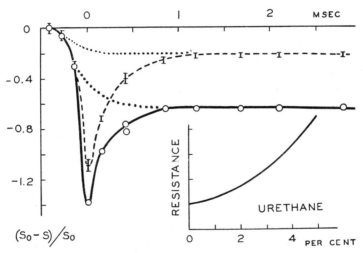

Fig. 38. Curve of the threshold reduction induced by a rectangular pulse of 180 mV applied to the myelin-covered stretch of a nerve fiber, when the myelinated portion was in normal ringer (the continuous line) and when it was in a 5 per cent urethane-ringer solution (the broken line). Inset: The relation between the D.C.-resistance of the myelin sheath and the concentration of urethane. The resistance was derived from the steady levels of the threshold reduction curves. Temperature 14°C. (From Maruyama, 1942.)

of two components, namely, the transient initial peak and the D.C. component. The threshold reduction curve can correspondingly be divided into two parts, as shown by the dotted lines in the figure. It is exclusively the D.C. component that is affected by the narcotic. On several occasions, it was verified directly with an oscillograph that the transient leakage of the action current through the myelin sheath is not affected by this narcotic to any appreciable extent.

The effect of narcotics upon the D.C. resistance of the myelin sheath was found to increase with increasing concentration. But, this property of narcotics did not seem to have anything to do with the "narcotizing" effect of those chemicals. Dealing with cocaine, it was found that an increase in the resistance of the myelin sheath becomes perceptible only at concentrations above 0.25 per cent, whereas the ability of the node to develop an action current is completely suppressed at a concentration as low as

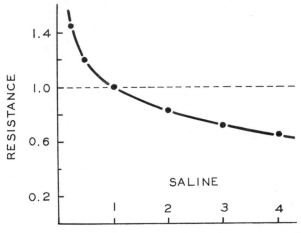

Fig. 39. The relation between the D.C.-resistance of the myelin sheath and the concentration of saline solution. Ordinates, resistance of the myelin sheath in arbitrary unit derived from the steady level of the threshold reduction curve. Abscissae, osmotic pressure of the saline solution, that of normal ringer being taken as unity. The composition of salts was the same as that of normal ringer. Temperature 13°C. (From Maruyama, 1942.)

0.005 per cent. In case of urethane, a complete narcosis of the node takes place at concentrations higher than about 3 per cent.

The effect of electrolytes (NaCl, CaCl₂, KCl) on the resistance of the myelin sheath is opposite to that of narcotics. The D.C. resistance of the myelin sheath is decreased by addition of electrolytes in ringer fluid and is increased by dilution of ringer fluid with water (Fig. 39). Among electrolytes, the behavior of KCl is somewhat peculiar; addition of this substance in ringer fluid changes, unlike others, and resting threshold (S_0) for the adjacent

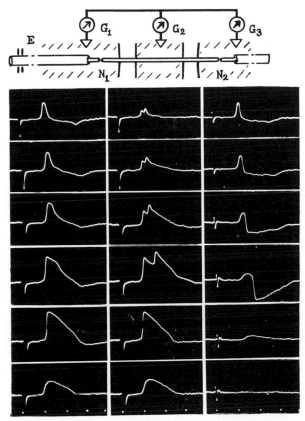

Fig. 40. The changes in the configuration of action currents of a single nerve fiber brought about by application of 2.5 per cent saponin-ringer solution to the myelinated portion of fiber. The records in the left column were taken with the amplifier connected in the position labelled G_1 in the diagram on the top; the records in the middle column were taken with G_2, and those in the right column with G_3. The three records on the top were taken when the fiber was immersed in normal ringer. The records in 2nd to 6th rows were taken 10, 23, 32, 35 and 37 minutes, respectively, after introduction of saponin solution into the middle pool. Time marks, 1 millisecond apart. The spike-height of the action current in the middle, top, amounts to 1.2×10^{-9} ampere. Temperature 16°C. (From *Arch. Intern. Stud. Neurol.*, 2:3.)

node immersed in normal ringer. The resistance-decreasing effect of CaCl$_2$ is less conspicuous than that of NaCl or KCl. The effect of these chemicals is completely reversible.

Addition of various non-electrolytes, such as glucose, saccharose, urea, etc., in ringer fluid was shown to bring about practically no effect upon the resistance of the myelin sheath, even when the concentration was such that the osmotic pressure of the solution was four times that of normal ringer.

5. THE EFFECT OF SAPONIN AND OTHER CHEMICALS UPON THE MYELIN SHEATH

The effect of saponin and soaps upon the myelin sheath is interesting in regard to the insulating property of this sheath. These are thought of as chemicals which are capable of mildly dissolving fatty substance covering living cells. Application of these chemicals, therefore, upon the myelin-covered portion of the nerve fiber is expected to remove the myelin substance and to render electric insulation of the axis-cylinder less perfect.

Direct experimental evidence has been acquired indicating that these chemicals actually augment the leakage of action current through the myelin sheath. With the experimental set-up shown by the diagram of Figure 40, top, a 2.5 per cent saponin-ringer solution was introduced into the middle small pool in which the myelin-covered portion of a fiber was immersed and action currents were recorded through this portion of the nerve fiber from time to time.

Following introduction of saponin into the middle pool, the action current led through the myelin sheath undergoes progressive augmentation. With increasing leakage through the myelin sheath, the transmission-time across this internodal segment increases. Finally, at one moment, transmission of impulse across this internodal segment is suddenly and completely blocked.

It goes without saying that an increase in the leakage of action current through the myelin sheath reduces the strength of the outward-directed current through the node N$_2$ on the distal side of the poisoned region. When this outward-directed current falls below the threshold, the impulse fails to jump across this internodal segment.

Besides these fat-dissolving agents, strong alkalis, acids, pure

ether and many other chemicals destroy the myelin-covered portion of the nerve fiber very readily, causing block of transmission.
But the effect of all these chemicals mentioned above, including
saponin and soaps, is irreversible.   The only chemical which is
known to block transmission reversibly when applied locally on
the myelin-covered portion of a nerve fiber is a dilute NH_3-ringer
solution.   Application of about 0.001 per cent NH_3 solution decreases the strengths of all the action currents led from the site of
application with three different electrode-arrangements (G_1, G_2,
and G_3 in Fig. 40).   Block of transmission occurs in a very short
time after application of NH_3.   In this stage, the threshold for
the fiber, measured with currents passing through the NH_3-treated
region, was found to be distinctly higher than that for the normal
fiber.   The NH_3-molecules seem to penetrate the myelin sheath
very readily and to change the colloidal state of the axoplasm.
One of the plausible explanations of the block by NH_3 seems to be
to ascribe it to "an increased electrical resistance" for the currents
passing across the NH_3-treated region of the nerve fiber.

CHAPTER VI

TRANSMISSION DURING THE REFRACTORY PERIOD

I. PROPERTIES OF THE NODE DURING REFRACTORINESS

For determining the threshold of a nerve fiber in all the experiments stated up to this time, we have repeatedly applied electric current pulses to the fiber at intervals of 1 to 20 seconds. In so doing, we have been fully convinced that the state of the nerve fiber is scarcely affected by the previous activity. It is because of this property that we can carry out precise quantitative measurements on the nerve fiber. If, however, the interval of these stimulating pulses is reduced below about 10 milliseconds at room temperature, we find immediately that, following production of an action current, there is a period during which the property of the nerve fiber is considerably different from that in the resting state. This period is generally known as the *refractory period* of the nerve fiber.

Our work in this chapter is to clarify how a nerve impulse is transmitted along a nerve fiber during the refractory period. We know that, in the normal, or non-refractory, nerve fiber, transmission is effected through excitation of individual nodes of Ranvier by action currents from the adjacent nodes. Hence, a thorough investigation of the behavior of the individual node of Ranvier following activity can be expected to provide us with rigid bases on which we can consider transmission in a refractory nerve fiber. We shall therefore devote this section to a description of the properties of the node during refractoriness.

If a single node of Ranvier, isolated by means of bridge-insulators and cocaine as usual, is excited by rectangular voltage pulses delivered at varying intervals after a supra-threshold induction shock (see the diagram in Fig. 41), it is found that the threshold for the node is higher and the action current from this node is weaker in the refractory period than in the resting state. For a quantitative investigation of the threshold and the action current of a refractory node, the use of such paired stimuli (an induction shock followed by a rectangular pulse) applied repeatedly at a relatively long interval (1 to 20 seconds) is very serviceable. An example of the results obtained by this method is seen in Figure 41.

It is seen in this figure that, even in the refractory period, the action current is released from the node in roughly all-or-none manner; that is to say, a barely supra-threshold stimulus elicits a full-sized response from the node. At any given moment during the refractory period, the size of the response was found to be practically independent of the strength of the second stimulus. As the time elapses after production of a response, both the threshold of the node and the size of response are gradually restored to normal.

The whole course of the recovery along which the threshold and the size of response are restored in the refractory period is shown in Figure 42. In this figure, the threshold voltage (S) and the spike-height of the action current (A) are plotted against the time from the first (conditioning) shock to the end of the second rectangular pulse. In light of our finding that, with stimulating pulses of this

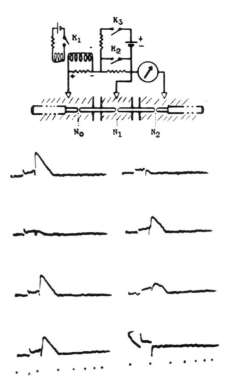

Fig. 41. Above: Diagram of the experimental arrangement to record action current from single node of Ranvier in the refractory period. The node N_1 is immersed in normal ringer fluid, and the nodes in the two lateral pools (N_0, N_2, and others) are kept in a 0.3 per cent cocaine-ringer solution.

Below: Some of the action current records taken with the arrangement above. The intervals from the first (induction) shock to the second (rectangular) shock and the strengths of the second shock are, from left top downwards, about 10 sec. and 62 mV., 4.2 msec. and 60 mV., 4.2 msec. and 62 mV., 3.2 msec. and 72 mV., from right top downwards, 2.6 msec. and 88 mV., 2.6 msec. and 89 mV., 2.2 msec. and 124 mV., 1.7 msec. and 150 mV. Time msec. 22°C. (From *Pflügers Arch.*, 245:464.)

duration, the spike-height of the normal action current is about five times as strong as the stimulating current of the threshold strength, the recovery curve for the spike-height is so constructed that it approaches towards the end of the refractory period the level of five times the threshold. The time-course of such a recovery curve is practically independent of the strength of the first shock, provided that it is not very close to threshold.

These curves have an interesting feature. All during the course of recovery, the spike-height of action current (A) seems to vary inversely as the threshold (S). At a definite moment which is labeled R in the figure, the threshold becomes infinite and the ac-

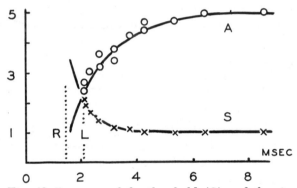

Fig. 42. Recovery of the threshold (S) and the size of the action current (A) following delivery of a supra-threshold induction shock. Abscissa, the time from the start of the first stimulus (induction shock) to the end of the second stimulus (rectangular pulse of 0.5 msec. duration). Some of the records from which the data for this graph have been taken are reproduced in the preceding figure. (From *Pflügers Arch.*, 245:772.)

tion current correspondingly becomes zero. The period during which no response whatsoever is elicitable (namely from 0 to R in the figure) is generally termed the "absolutely refractory period," and the later stage in the refractory period is called the "relatively refractory period."

2. THE LEAST INTERVAL BETWEEN TWO IMPULSES

Let us now consider what will happen if we apply two relatively strong induction shocks at a short interval to a nerve fiber im-

mersed in normal ringer solution.   To be concrete in our discussion, we shall take the experimental arrangement of Figure 43,
top.   With this arrangement, delivery of the first shock is certain
to initiate an impulse at the node N_1 in the figure.   If a long interval separates the first and the second shocks, there is no doubt

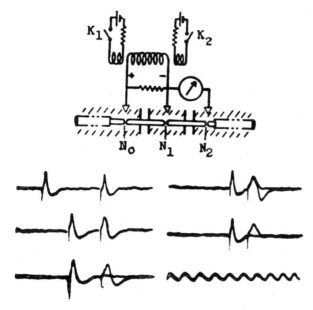

Fig. 43. Records of action currents induced in a
nerve fiber immersed in normal ringer by two induction shocks applied at varying intervals.   The
strength of the first shock was constant (slightly
above threshold).   The strengths of the second
shocks were, from the record on the left-hand top
downwards, 1 (threshold), 1.45, 1.3 and 1.35 (the
last two records being superposed on the same film);
from right-hand top downwards, 2.1 (two successive
sweeps on the same film at the same stimulus
strength), 2.1 (subthreshold) and 2.2 (superposed
on the same film).   Time marker, 1000 cycles per
sec.   Large afferent fiber arising in the toad muscle,
at 23°C.

that the second shock also initiates an impulse at this node.   If,
in the next place, the second shock falls in the absolutely refractory period left behind the first impulse, the second shock is expected not to elicit any detectable response in the fiber.

We have seen in the last section that, immediately after the end of the absolutely refractory period, a strong stimulus elicits from the node a very small response. With the arrangement of Figure 43, top, such a small response elicited from the node N_1 is expected to act as a stimulating current upon the neighboring node N_2; but as the latter node is evidently of extremely high threshold at this moment, it is certain that this small response fails to excite the node N_2. It is thus inferred that, unless the second response is elicited in a later stage during the relatively refractory period, the response would be localized at the site of stimulation and would fail to be propagated on both sides.

An example of the experimental results obtained under these conditions is seen in Figure 43. At the stimulation interval of 1.6 milliseconds, a second response could be induced at the primary node (N_1 in the figure) in practically all-or-none manner, but this response showed no sign of transmission to the next node N_2. Only at intervals longer than 1.7 milliseconds in this preparation, induction shocks of supra-threshold strength provoked action currents of the diphasic configuration which was unquestionably indicative of transmission from the primary to the secondary node.

We now know that there is in the relatively refractory period a critical shortest interval at which a second propagated impulse can be evoked. We can roughly estimate this critical interval from the diagram of the preceding figure. At the moment when the two curves S and A in the figure intersect each other, the action current developed by the primary node is sufficient to act upon the secondary node as a stimulus of the threshold strength. This time of intersection of the two curves is therefore expected to coincide with the least interval between two impulses elicitable in this fiber, although the consideration of the latency in electrical excitation and the form of the action current as stimulus appear to make our argument somewhat dubious.

Assuming the action current from a refractory node to vary inversely as the threshold of this node, it is found that the two curves in Figure 42 should cross when the action current is $1/\sqrt{5}$ times the normal strength and the threshold is $\sqrt{5}$ times the resting value. From this it follows that the response which is capable of transmission along a refractory nerve fiber should be greater than approximately 40 per cent of the normal size.

For normal nerve fibers, as is seen in Figure 42, the difference between the duration of the absolutely refractory period and the least interval in the sense stated above is very small. This difference becomes very significant in the discussion of transmission along a narcotized nerve fiber which will be referred to later.

3. THE BEHAVIOR OF THE SECOND IMPULSE

If one sends into a nerve fiber two induction shocks at a short interval and records the second impulse at some distance from the

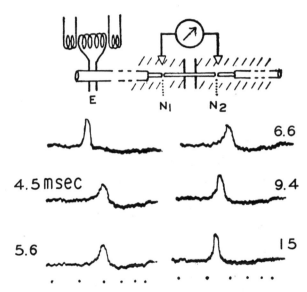

Fig. 44. Action currents accompanying impulses elicited during the relatively refractory period. The intervals between the two induction shocks applied through the electrodes E are given. The record at the upper left-hand corner was taken with a single shock. Time, in msec.; temperature 12°C. (From *Pflügers Arch.*, 245:773.)

site of stimulation, one finds at once (1st) that the action current associated with the second impulse is smaller and more diphasic than that accompanying the first impulse and (2nd) that the shock-response interval for the second impulse is much longer than that for the first impulse (Fig. 44). As regards the size of the response, it may be sufficient to mention that the time-interval, which intervenes between the arrival of the first impulse at the position of the lead-off electrodes and the arrival of the second action current, is the factor which determines the size of the

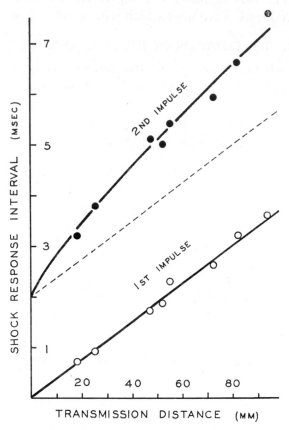

Fig. 45. The relation between the transmission-distance and the shock-response interval for two impulses released at an interval of 2 msec. A nerve fiber of 11 microns in diameter innervating *m. flexor digitorum brevis* of the toad. Temperature 23°C.

second response. Both the increased diphasicity and the lengthened shock-response interval are the phenomena resulting from increased internodal transmission-time in the refractory nerve fiber.

In the transmission of the second impulse, every node of Ranvier of the fiber is excited by relatively weak stimulating current developed by the adjacent partially refractory node. In the refractory node as well as in the resting node, the latency of the action current becomes longer as the strength of the stimulating current is brought nearer the threshold at that moment. Since the threshold is higher in the relatively refractory node than in the normal one, the increase of the internodal transmission-time by partial refractoriness is an entirely intelligible phenomenon. If the action-e.m.f. at the node N_2 in Figure 44 is to start after the current developed by the node N_1 has subsided to a considerable extent, the start of the activity at the node N_2 should result in reversal of the current flowing through the current registering device.

The fact that the second impulse is transmitted at a slower rate than the first impulse leads us to expect the following phenomenon: As two impulses travel along the fiber, the second one lags behind the first, resulting in an increase of the separation between the first and the second impulses; this in turn causes the second impulse to travel faster and faster, a greater separation allowing a more complete recovery from refractoriness.

This phenomenon is shown to actually occur by the experimental data of Figure 45, which is nothing more than confirmation of a similar experiment made by Gasser and Erlanger (1925) for the whole nerve. In this diagram, the distance between the stimulating electrodes E and the exposed node N_1 in Figure 44 are plotted as abscissae against the time-intervals from the delivery of the first induction shock to the arrivals of the first or the second impulse at the node N_1 as ordinates. At the site of stimulation, the two impulses are made to start at a constant interval of 2 milliseconds.

The linearity between the transmission-distance and the shock-response interval for the first impulse attests to the constancy of the rate of transmission of the first impulse. If the second impulse were transmitted along the fiber at the same rate as the first one, the relation between the transmission-distance and the shock-response interval would be expressed by the broken straight line in the figure. The slope of the curve connecting the solid circles in the figure indicates very clearly that the rate of the second impulse is quite low at its start (approximately half the normal rate) and gradually approaches the normal rate during transmission.

4. THE SPIKE-DURATION AND THE REFRACTORY PERIOD

Let us now compare the duration of the action current, or the spike-duration, with the length of the absolutely refractory period. We have seen that the action current from a single node of Ran-

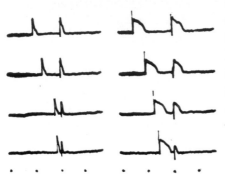

vier is practically independent of the strength and duration of the stimulating current pulse. From this it follows that a stimulus applied to a node during action should be practically ineffective in setting up a new response.[*] Therefore, the question to be answered is: How long is the interval from the end of the spike to the beginning of the relatively refractory period?

Working mainly with slower excitable tissues such as heart and skeletal muscle, Adrian established in 1921 that the end of the action current (spike) always coincides with the beginning of the relatively refractory period. With single nodes of Ranvier of the toad myelinated fiber, it was found that this law of Adrian's holds with fair accuracy for its action current. In Figure 46, we have an example of experi-

Fig. 46. Left column: Responses of a single node of Ranvier in normal ringer fluid elicited by two induction shocks delivered at varying intervals. Neighboring nodes had been treated with a 0.2 per cent cocaine-ringer solution. The strengths of the second induction shock (barely supra-threshold at that moment) were, from the top downwards, 1, 1.1, 1.7 and 2.05.

Right column: Same but about 15 minutes after application of a 0.5 per cent sinomenine-ringer solution on the node under investigation. The strengths of the second shocks, from the top downwards, 1.12, 1.2, 1.6 and 2.4. A large motor nerve fiber of the toad at 23.5°C. Time marks, 5 msec. apart.

---

[*] It has been shown by the method of threshold reduction that a very strong current pulse imposed upon the node in action modifies the configuration of the action current (Tasaki, 1940). Later on, with an amplifier and a cathode ray tube, it was shown directly that the action current from a single node of Ranvier was curtailed considerably by the passage of a strong inward-directed current pulse in the early stage of activity of the node.

ments undertaken to test this point for a node under normal as well as sinomenine-poisoned state. It is seen in this figure that the second response is elicitable very soon after the end of the first spike.

Besides sinomenine and its allied alkaloids (brucine, emetine and heroine), lowering the temperature has been shown to markedly lengthen the spike-duration. It was shown recently that the temperature coefficient for the process of recovery of threshold coincides practically perfectly with that for the spike-duration, both of them being approximately 3.5 for the change of 10° (Tasaki, 1949). At every temperature, the interval from the end of the first spike to the earliest second response (obtained by extrapolation) was found to be less than 15 per cent of the total spike-duration.

CHAPTER VII

TRANSMISSION IN THE NARCOTIZED FIBER

I. NARCOSIS OF A SINGLE NODE

In all the experiments stated up to this time, narcotizing solutions were employed with a view to depriving the nerve fiber, or a part of it, of its ability to develop action current. We know however that, in the adequate range of concentration, these narcotics depress the function of the node of Ranvier to an extent that depends upon the concentration. The purpose of our work in this chapter is to figure out the mechanism of nervous transmission between such partially, or incompletely, narcotized nodes.

Let us first examine, just as we did in our study on the transmission between refractory nodes, the effect of this agent upon a single node of Ranvier and then try to deduce the interaction among these abnormal nodes.

The records of action currents furnished in Figure 47 show the effect of dilute urethane-ringer solutions upon a single node of Ranvier. A large motor nerve fiber of the toad was laid across two bridge-insulators, and the portions of the fiber in the two lateral pools were treated with a 0.2 per cent cocaine-ringer solution which completely narcotized all the nodes of the fiber except the one in the middle (N_1). When this node was immersed in normal ringer fluid, a record was taken of the action current induced by a rectangular pulse of the threshold strength. Then, the fluid in the middle pool was replaced with urethane solution of varying concentrations and, at every concentration, the size of the response and the threshold of the node were determined.

It was discovered by this method that the threshold and the magnitude of the response of the node are immediately modified by the narcotic to the extent determined by the concentration employed and, as long as the concentration remains constant, both the threshold and the size of the response remain practically constant. In other words, *the equilibrium between the narcotic and the excitable plasma membrane is attained in immeasurably short time.* In this respect, typical narcotics (urethane, cocaine, ethanol etc.) are in marked contrast with chloral hydrate, veratrine, sinomenine and others, which progressively modify the threshold and the action current of the node. With the typical narcotics recovery from narcosis (ensuing from replacement of the narcotic with normal ringer fluid) is also very quick, although the restored level falls in general short of the normal excitability level.

Using short current pulses as stimulus, an incompletely narcotized node is found to develop action currents in practically all-or-none manner. With stimulating pulses of slightly above threshold, the response of the node starts, as can be seen in the figure, towards the end of the stimulating pulse. With much stronger stimuli, the node is brought in action after a shorter latency.

The dependence of the threshold (S) and the magni-

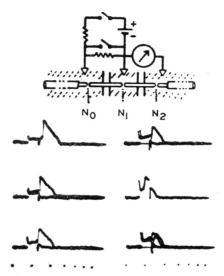

Fig. 47. The effect of urethane upon a single node of Ranvier. The nodes in the lateral pools (N_0 and N_2) are treated with a 0.2 per cent cocaine-ringer solution. The concentrations of the urethane-ringer solutions applied to the node in the middle and the strengths of stimuli are, from left top downwards, 0 per cent and 58 mV.; 0.75 per cent, 90 and 82 mV. (superposed); 1 per cent 92 and 94 mV. (superposed); from right top downwards, 1.5 per cent, 117 and 120 mV; 1.5 per cent and 170 mV.; 1.75 per cent, 135, 137 and 139 mv. Time markers, one msec. apart. Temperature 23.5°C. (From *Pflügers Arch.,* *246*:32, 1942.)

tude of action current (A) upon the concentration of urethane is seen in Figure 48, in which the normal size of action current is taken, just as we did in the case of the refractory node, as being equivalent to five times the normal threshold. Here again it is seen that the size of response varies inversely as the threshold. At strong concentrations, only small electrical responses are elicitable with very strong stimulating currents, and consequently

accurate measurements are not possible. Furthermore, it is
known that, in threshold excitation of a deeply, but not completely,
narcotized node, queer responses with variable size and duration
are evoked by long stimulating pulses (Tasaki and Mizuguchi,
1948). Those variable responses, however, do not seem to have
any important bearing on the problem of transmission of impulse
from node to node.

Before describing the effect of narcotics upon the excitable
mechanism, we should have clarified their effect upon the resting
state of the plasma membrane. The effect of cocaine and urethane upon the resistance of
the plasma membrane at the
first by the method of measuring the spread of stimulating
current across a node (Tasaki,
1939c) and next by the method
of impedance measurement
(Tasaki and Mizuguchi,
1949). All the experiments
unanimously told us that the
resistance through the nodal
plasma membrane is practically unaffected by narcosis.
The result of impedance measurement indicated that a 0.2
per cent cocaine-ringer solution introduced into one of the
two pools of a bridge-insulator increases the impedance of this
fiber by about 4 per cent or less. Even this increase seems
to be ascribable to the change of the myelin sheath and not the
effect of narcotic upon the nodal plasma membrane. On a good
many occasions, we have seen that the threshold for a node is
scarcely changed by application of narcotics upon the adjacent
nodes. This is a clear indication that the resting electromotive
force at the plasma membrane remains unaffected by narcosis,
because any change in the electromotive force at a node should
cause a current-flow through the neighboring nodes and its effect
should be detected by measuring the threshold (compare with the
effect of KCl shown in Fig. 73). Thus, we conclude that 0.01 to

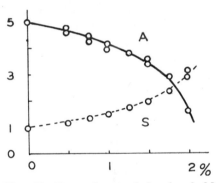

Fig. 48. Dependence of the threshold
(S) and the size of response (A) upon
the concentration of the urethane-
ringer solution, constructed from the
result of the experiment shown in
Figure 47 (From *Pflügers Arch.*, 245:
775.)

0.2 per cent cocaine-ringer solution completely inhibits production of action currents without changing the resting state of the fiber. It is because of this property that we could employ narcotics for the analysis of the function of individual nodes of Ranvier.

2. THE RATE OF TRANSMISSION ALONG A NARCOTIZED NERVE FIBER

We have seen in the preceding section that light narcosis of a node of Ranvier raises the threshold of the node and reduces the action current developed by the node. From this it immediately follows that the rate of transmission should be smaller in the narcotized region of a fiber than in the normal region.[*] Furthermore, since narcotics are shown to act promptly upon the exposed node, this slowing of the transmission should take place immediately after the application of a narcotizing solution to the operated region of a single fiber preparation.

The records furnished in Figure 49 show the legitimacy of the above argument. These were obtained by applying induction shocks of twice the threshold strength to the unoperated (proximal) region of a single fiber preparation before, during and after the application of 1.2 per cent urethane-ringer solution to the operated region. The action currents were led from the distal intact portion of the preparation close to the operated region. It is seen in this figure that the transmission is hampered immediately after application of the narcotic to the fiber to the extent depending upon the concentration of the narcotic employed. The recovery from narcosis is seen to be very quick.

When a narcotic is applied to the intact, unoperated region of a single fiber preparation, the narcotic is considered to diffuse gradually into the interior of the nerve bundle and consequently to retard the transmission progressively. This can easily be demonstrated by the following procedure taking muscular contractions as our index:

---

[*] In excitation of an incompletely narcotized node by long rectangular voltage pulses of varying strengths, the strength-latency relation is given, as in the case of the normal node, by the formula $v = b(1 + k/t)$, b being the rheobase at that state of the node. The value of the constant k for a narcotized node is slightly smaller than that for a normal. This change in the constant k tends to increase the rate of transmission in the narcotized region of a nerve fiber, although in reality this effect is masked by the more conspicuous effects on the rheobase and on the size of the response.

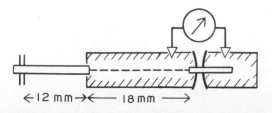

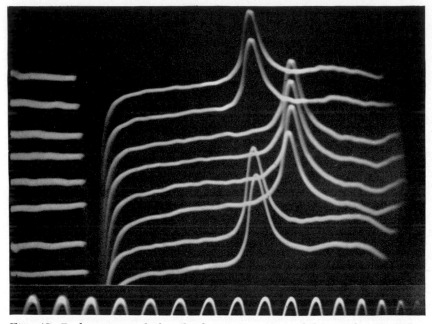

Fig. 49. Prolongation of the shock-response interval by application of a 1.2 per cent urethane-ringer solution upon the operated region of a single fiber preparation. Photographs were taken at interval of 90 seconds before, during and after narcosis, starting from the lowermost record. The fluid in the narcotizing chamber was replaced with the narcotic in the interval between the second (from the bottom) and the third recording and brought back to normal ringer in the interval between the sixth and seventh recording. The pronounced shock artefacts in these records are due to the presence of inactive tissues around the fiber under investigation between the two lead electrodes. A large motor nerve fiber innervating the toad sartorius muscle. Temperature 23°C. Time 0.2 msec.

As shown by the diagram of Figure 50, a portion of the nerve trunk of a nerve fiber-muscle preparation is introduced into a narcotizing chamber, and outside this chamber are arranged three pairs of platinum electrodes. Keeping the operated region of the preparation moist in normal ringer fluid, application of a supra-threshold induction shock to the nerve through one of these three pairs of electrodes evokes naturally a visible contraction in the muscle. Application of two induction shocks, say, the first shock through the electrodes E_1 in the figure and the second shock through E_3 at an interval of about 10 milliseconds after the delivery of the first shock, causes in the muscle a contraction distinctly more powerful than that caused by a single shock. When the interval between these shocks is decreased step by step, one finds that the strong contraction suddenly changes into a feeble

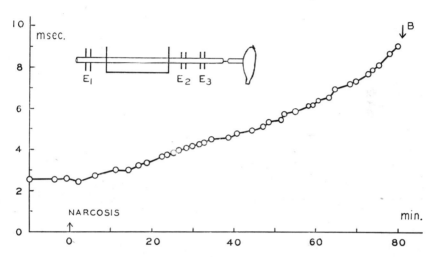

Fig. 50. Prolongation of the time required for transmission (between E_1 and E_2) by narcosis. The transmission-time (ordinate) was obtained by subtraction of the least effective stimulation interval measured with the electrodes E_2 and E_3 from that taken with E_1 and E_3. The length of the nerve between E_1 and E_2 was 45mm. and the length of the narcotized region was 40mm. Transmission through the narcotized region was blocked 80 minutes after the onset of narcosis. A large motor nerve fiber innervating the toad gastrocnemius muscle. Temperature 18°C.

one at a certain critical interval, showing that the second shock falls at this interval in the refractoriness left behind by the first impulse at the site of the electrodes E_3. The determination of the least effective interval between these two shocks by this technique can be carried out with great precision if the strength of the first shock is two to three times and the second shock four to five times the threshold at that locus. Subtraction of the least effective interval determined with the electrodes E_2 and E_3 from that obtained with E_1 and E_3 gives undoubtedly the time required for an impulse to travel between the electrodes E_1 and E_2. This

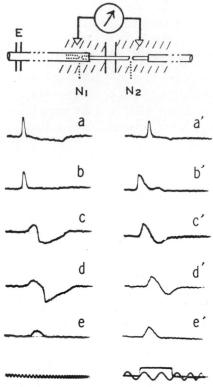

Fig. 51. Left column: (a), normal binodal action current induced by an induction shock applied through the electrode E. (b), record taken soon after introduction of a 1.4 per cent urethane-ringer solution into the distal (right) pool. (c), (d) and (e); 8.6, 10 and 10.2 minutes, respectively, after introduction of a 4.0 per cent urethane-ringer solution into the proximal pool. A large motor fiber of the toad at 14°C. Note that N_1 is not exposed. 5000 cycles per sec.

Right column: (a'), normal binodal record. (b'), after application of a 1.6 per cent urethane-Ringer solution on the distal portion. (c'), (d') and (e'); 5, 18.8 and 19.2 minutes, respectively, after application of a 3 per cent urethane-ringer solution to the proximal portion. A large bull frog fiber, at 17.5°C. Bottom, 1000 cycles per sec. and 10^{-9} ampere.

is the principle of the method of measuring the rate of nervous transmission which was pioneered by Bramwell and Lucas (1911).

With the experimental set-up shown in Figure 50, top, it is observed that the time required for transmission of impulse from E_1 to E_2 increases progressively as the time elapses. When the narcotizing solution was stronger, the progress of narcosis was found to be more rapid.

In all the experiments of this type, it is found that the nervous transmission can not be retarded indefinitely by narcosis but it is suddenly and completely blocked at a moment when the rate of transmission is reduced to 3 to 5 meters per second at room temperature. We shall consider in the following two sections how the nervous transmission is blocked by narcosis.

3. SUSPENSION OF NERVOUS TRANSMISSION BY NARCOSIS

In view of the mechanism of nervous transmission and the effect of narcotics upon the nerve fiber which we have figured out on the preceding pages, it is evident that the suspension of transmission occurs when the action current developed by a node of Ranvier is reduced by narcosis to such an extent that it falls short of the already heightened threshold of the adjacent node. From the diagram of Figure 48, it is expected that this occurs when the concentration of the narcotic used is such that the action current is reduced to slightly below one half and the threshold is raised to above twice the normal value. This conclusion, that narcotized nerve fiber which is incapable of carrying an impulse can still develop action current of nearly half the normal size in all-or-none manner, is very significant, because we could not even imagine such a result before the roles of the nodes in the nervous transmission were brought to light by the micro-technique.

The experiments of Figure 51 were undertaken in the hope of providing direct evidence for the conclusion of our argument stated above. After ordinary binodal action currents have been recorded from normal single fiber preparations mounted on a bridge-insulator (record a or a′), a relatively dilute urethane-ringer solution is introduced into the pool on the distal side of the bridge-insulator (record b or b′). Then the fluid in the proximal pool is replaced with a concentrated urethane-ringer solution, and records of action currents are taken from time to time until transmission across the bridge-insulator is suddenly suspended.

In favorable cases, action current records can be obtained by this technique showing approximately equal upward and downward deflections immediately before suspension of transmission (record d′). The upward deflection in this figure is unquestionably derived mainly from the activity of the node N_1 and the downward deflection from N_2. The equality of the size of these two deflections may be taken as reproducing the condition for suspension of transmission in the uniformly narcotized region of a nerve fiber. The fact that the size of action current observed under such circumstances amounts to approximately half the normal value attests undoubtedly to the legitimacy of our argument.

We know that, in threshold excitation of a node by a current pulse of 0.5 to 2 milliseconds in duration, action currents start toward the end of the stimulating pulse. It follows from this that, immediately before suspension of transmission by uniform narcosis of a nerve fiber, the internodal transmission-time should be approximately equal to the duration of the action current at that

condition.   Judging by the results of record d′ of Figure 51 and
also by the records in Figure 47, the duration of the action current
at that condition is considered to be 0.5 to 1 millisecond at room
temperature.   Thus, we have arrived at a rough but satisfactory
explanation of the experimental results stated in the preceding
section that the slowest critical rate of transmission in a narcotized
nerve fiber is of the order of 3 to 5 meters per second.

We have seen in the preceding section further that, when a
narcotic is applied to an intact nerve, narcosis deepens as the
narcotic diffuses into the nerve trunk and transmission is blocked
at the moment when the concentration of the narcotic around
the fiber reaches a certain critical level.   Therefore, the higher
the concentration outside the nerve, the more rapidly should the
concentration of the narcotic rise inside the nerve bundle.   Diffusion of narcotics into the intact nerve bundle is greatly hindered
by the connective tissue sheath surrounding the nerve.   Operative
removal of this sheath reduces the time required for suspension
of transmission down to a half of the normal value or still less.   If
we assume this sheath to be the main barrier to the diffusion, then
it is expected that the concentration inside the nerve rises exponentially as the time after application of the narcotic, namely, $u =
C(1 - e^{-kt})$, where u denotes the concentration inside the nerve
at the moment t, C the concentration of the narcotic applied to the
nerve from outside and k the diffusion constant through the connective tissue sheath.   Denoting the critical concentration by g
and the time required for suspension of transmission by T, we find
that the relation between C and T should be given by $g =
C(1 - e^{-kT})$.

Working with urethane-ringer solutions of below 9 per cent
applied to the sciatic (whole) nerve of the toad, Tsukagoshi
(1944) has actually demonstrated, in Keio Physiological Institute, that the experimental results are in complete accordance with
the exponential formula stated above (Fig. 52).   He determined
the critical concentration directly by teasing the nerve for a
length of 15 millimeters and applying narcotics of varying concentrations to this part of nerve.   He obtained an average value
of 2.0 per cent for the critical concentration at that condition of
the experiment.   Adopting this value, he found that the observed
results can be expressed satisfactorily by choosing the arbitrary
constant k to be 0.023 min^{-1} (the continuous curve in Fig. 52).

In the experiments with cocaine-ringer solutions, however, he found it difficult to reconcile the observed data with the simple formula above. In the case of cocaine, we have to use concentrations of 50 to 500 times as high as the critical value g (about 0.01 per cent), owing to the sluggishness of penetration of this narcotic into the nerve. Under these circumstances, we have

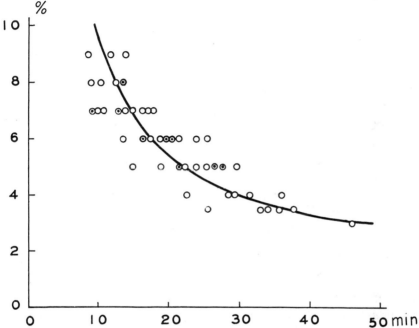

Fig. 52. The relation between the concentration of urethane-ringer solution applied to sciatic nerves of the toad (ordinate) and the time required for suspension of transmission through the narcotized region (abscissa). The length of the narcotized region was 15 mm., and the diameter of the nerves employed was between 0.96 and 1.1 mm. Room temperature was between 9 and 11°C. The continuous curve is drawn according to the equation
$$C \left(1 - e^{-0.023T}\right) = 2.$$
(From *Tsukagoshi,* 1944.)

to solve a complicated differential equation to express the relation between concentration and time to suspension of transmission.

4. TRANSMISSION OF A NERVE IMPULSE FROM NORMAL TO A NARCOTIZED REGION OF NERVE FIBER

In the consideration of the effect of a narcotic applied to a limited length of a nerve fiber, we have to pay attention to the transitional phenomenon which is expected to occur when an im-

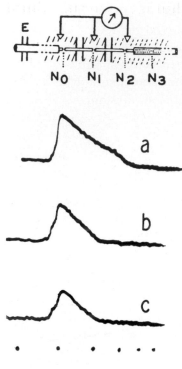

Fig. 53. Top: A large motor nerve fiber of the toad laid across a pair of bridge-insulators. a: Record taken with the portion of the fiber in the distal pool treated with 0.3 per cent cocaine ringer solution; other two pools were filled with normal ringer. b: Record taken after introduction of a 1.5 per cent urethane-ringer solution into the middle pool c: After replacing the fluid in the middle pool with a 1.7 per cent urethane-ringer solution. Temperature 18.5°C. Time marks 1 msec. apart.

pulse passes from a normal to a narcotized region. To obtain an idea of this phenomenon, let us take the following experiment.

A nerve fiber with three successive nodes of Ranvier exposed is laid across a pair of bridge-insulators as shown by the diagram in Figure 53, top. With the two proximal pools filled with normal ringer fluid and the distal pool (in which the node N_2 is immersed) with a concentrated cocaine-ringer solution, a record is taken of the action current which we believe to derive mainly from the activity of the node N_1 in the middle pool (record a). Application of a 1.5 per cent urethane-ringer solution to the portion of the fiber in the middle pool is found not only to reduce the size and duration of the observed action current but also to bring about a distinct notch on its ascending limb (record b).

It is evident in this record that the part of the deflection below the notch is due to spread of the current generated by the node N_0 in the proximal pool and that the notch is an indication of the start of activity at the incompletely narcotized node N_1 in the middle pool. From this it follows that the node N_2 in the figure is traversed, in this case, by an outward-directed current stronger than that caused either N_0 alone or N_1 alone.

It has been demonstrated, by the method of high frequency A.C. Wheatstone bridge, that the impedance loss during activity is much less in the narcotized fiber than in the normal (Tasaki and Mizuguchi, 1949). It is therefore obvious that the resistance through the active plasma membrane in the narcotized region of a nerve fiber is not very small and, as the consequence, that a strong current generated by a normal node spreads beyond several incompletely narcotized nodes. From this it follows that the transmission of an impulse near the entrance into the narcotized region should be considerably different from that in the normal or uniformly narcotized region of a nerve fiber.

This transitional change of the nerve impulse at the entrance of a narcotized region of nerve was first brought to light by professor Genichi Kato and Doctor Hallowell Davis, to whom this book is dedicated, and their collaborators (Kato, 1924 and 1926; Davis and Brunswick, 1926; Davis, Forbes, Brunswick and Hopkins, 1926). It has been their work that attracted the interest of the author of this book towards the mechanism of nervous transmission in the narcotized as well as normal nerve fiber.

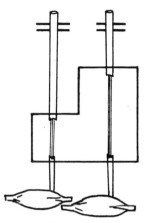

Fig. 54. Diagram of two sciatic - semitendinosus preparations taken from a toad, illustrating the operated regions introduced in a narcotizing chamber.

The transitional change of the nerve impulse at the entrance of the narcotized region manifests itself most conspicuously when we measure the time required for suspension of transmission after application of narcotics upon a limited length of nerve. Although this is clearly shown by the classical experiments done by Adrian (1912), we shall make mention in this place of Huruyama's experiment (1941) in which narcotics were applied to the operated region of "multi-fiber muscle preparations" (Fig. 54). Two sciatic-semitendinosus preparations were taken from both legs of a toad, and the connective tissue sheaths of the nerves were removed for different lengths. Introducing these two preparations in one and the same narcotizing chamber as shown in Figure 53, Huruyama observed that the time required for suspension of transmission through the narcotized region is always shorter in the preparation with the longer narcotized region than that with the shorter one. The following table shows some of the data he obtained using a 3 per cent urethane-ringer solution as the narcotic. It is clearly shown in this table that, with the narcotic applied to a length of nerve of about 10 millimeters, suspension of transmission sets in very quickly, whereas with shorter narcotized regions transmission is blocked only after a longer stretch of the fibers is included in narcosis by diffusion of the narcotic on both sides. It should be added in this place also that narcotizing solutions of above a certain critical concentration applied to a region of an isolated single nerve fiber longer than 10 millimeters, *block transmission almost instantaneously* after application (Tasaki and others in Kato's review, 1936; Huxley and Staempfli, 1950).

experiment	*narcotic on 6 mm.*	*narcotic on 3 mm.*
1	1 min. 50 sec.	3 min. 30 sec.
2	1 00	2 10
3	6 30	7 30
4	2 40	5 30

experiment	*narcotic on 10 mm.*	*narcotic on 4 mm.*
1	below 1 sec.	1 min. 20 sec.
2	20	3 10
3	50	10 20
4	30	4 20

The transitional change of the nerve impulse at the entrance of the narcotized region is evidently the cause of a group of phenomena, including the one just described, known by the name of "decrement" in the classical nerve physiology (see Lucas, 1917). A number of ingenious experiments done by Lucas and Adrian along this line have long been admired by the present author. As to the new explanations of those classical experiments, however, no special description seems to be necessary except for the experiments dealing with repetitive excitation of a narcotized nerve fiber which will be referred to in the following section.

5. WEDENSKY PHENOMENON

For the consideration of the effect of repetitive excitation of a narcotized nerve fiber, it is necessary for us to examine experi-

mentally the response of a single incompletely narcotized node
of Ranvier to repetitive stimulation. We have already dealt in
the preceding chapter with the behavior of a normal node in the
refractory phase. We shall now inquire into the effect of refractoriness upon the behavior of an incompletely narcotized node of
Ranvier.

With the experimental arrangement of Figure 41 described in
the early part of the preceding chapter (p. 81), we first examined

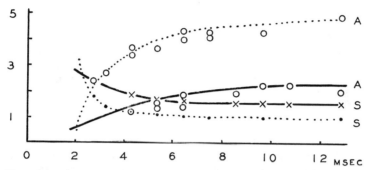

Fig. 55. The strength of action current (A) and the threshold
(S) during the refractory period obtained for a normal (dotted
curves) and incompletely narcotized (continuous curves) single
node of Ranvier.   Abscissa, time-interval from the start of the
first stimulus (induction shock) to the end of the second stimulus
(rectangular pulse of 0.5 msec.). The arrangement of Figure 41
was used. As the safety factor in the transmission is in the normal
fiber approximately 5, the strength of action current from non-
narcotized resting node is taken to 5 times the threshold for the
node.   Application of a 1.2 per cent urethane-ringer solution to
the node under investigation increased the threshold for the node
to approximately twice the normal resting level and reduced the
size of response down to approximately $^1/_2$ the normal resting
value.   A large motor fiber of the toad at 18.5°C. (From *Pflügers
Arch.*, 245:776.)

during the refractory period the size of response of a single normal node and the threshold of the node for rectangular stimulating
pulses of 0.5 millisecond in duration.   The result obtained is
shown by the dotted lines in Figure 55.   Then, a 1.2 per cent
urethane-ringer solution was introduced into the middle pool
where the node under investigation was immersed. By this procedure the resting threshold was raised up to twice the normal
value and the size of the response was reduced to a half the nor-

mal. Examination of the behavior of this node during the refractoriness left behind the first response (induced by an induction shock) yielded the result shown by the continuous curves in Figure 55. The response of the node was found, even under these circumstances, to be released approximately in all-or-none manner.

It is seen in this figure that, during the course of about 10 milliseconds after the start of the first response, the excitability of the node is still lower than the already low level in the narcotized state. In accordance with the fact that narcosis reduces the duration of the action current from a single node, the absolutely refractory period seems to be made shorter by narcosis. But, the time at which the two curves A and S intersect each other, namely, the least interval in the sense defined in the preceding chapter, is considerably lengthened by this dilute urethane solution. The physiological significance of the least interval is that the strength of the action current of the node elicited at this moment is just equal to the threshold strength of the stimulating current needed to induce a response in the fiber. The second response elicited from the node at this moment is just, and only just, effective in exciting the next node, provided that this latter node is equally narcotized and is in the same stage during the refractory period.

Because of this remarkable prolongation of the least interval by narcosis, the impulse induced during the refractory period in a uniformly narcotized nerve fiber shows a marked tendency to be localized at the nodes for which the stimulating current from outside, or the strong action current spreading from the non-narcotized region, has exercised a strong excitatory effect. The maximum size of the action current which can be localized at the site of stimulation by the mechanism stated above should be, just as in the case of localized response in a non-narcotized (but refractory) fiber, a little less than a half of the normal strength of action current in the resting fiber.

In terms of the diagram of Figure 55, it is possible to give rigid explanations of all the previous experiments dealing with repetitive stimulation of narcotized nerve fibers. A group of phenomena known as Wedensky inhibition, for which many explanations have already been proposed without carrying conviction, is doubtless due to rise of threshold (S) and reduction of the action current (A) during the refractory period. The smaller the interval between stimuli, the smaller becomes the ratio $A:S$. For such high frequency stimulation as to reduce the ratio $A:S$ to a value smaller than unity (but still above zero), the stimuli can not

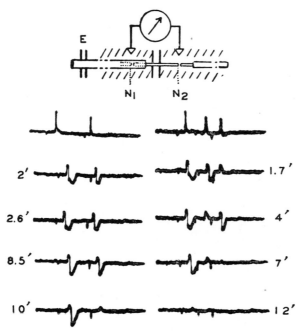

Fig. 56. The effect of a 4 per cent urethane-ringer solution introduced into the proximal pool (on the side of the N_1) upon the transmission of impulses sent into the fiber at intervals of 10 msec. (left column) and at 5 msec. (right column). The time from the onset of narcosis is given. A large motor fiber of the toad at 12.5°C. (From *Pflügers Arch.*, 245:778.)

elicit more than one propagated impulse, though they may induce responses at the site of stimulation if they are strong enough. In a non-narcotized nerve fiber, the time-interval between the end of the absolutely refractory period (at which $A:S = 0$) and the least interval (at which $A:S = 1$) is very small, and therefore it is difficult to investigate the effect left behind the localized response elicited during this period. In the narcotized node, it is easily demonstrated that repetitive stimulation at a high frequency sets up only one propagated impulse, whereas, with stimuli delivered at a low frequency, every one stimulus gives rise to one propagated impulse. There is good evidence to believe that the refractoriness left behind several responses induced in rapid succession is not very different from that represented by the curves in Figure 55.

The action current records furnished in Figure 56 give an example of the Wedensky phenomenon observed in the narcotized nerve fiber. It is seen in this figure that, at a certain stage of narcosis (seven minutes after the onset of narcosis in this case), the second and third impulses arriving at the narcotized region at an interval of 5 milliseconds failed to pass through the narcotized region while the one following the first at intervals of 10 milliseconds traveled along the fiber without being blocked.

CHAPTER VIII

THE EFFECT OF ELECTROTONUS ON TRANSMISSION

1. THE PROPERTIES OF THE NODE UNDER ELECTROTONUS

Like other physical and chemical agents, the passage of a steady current through a portion of a nerve fiber is known to modify the state of the fiber. The state of the fiber under the influence of a constant current can be disclosed by application of another current pulse of a short duration which may, if strong enough, elicit a response from the fiber. Under these circumstances, we may regard only the second, testing current pulse as "stimulus" and speak of the threshold and the action current of the fiber as modified by a steady current. As our current registering device, namely, the condenser-coupled amplifier used in conjunction with an oscillograph, is insensitive to a steady component of current, we mean by the stimulating and action currents the currents observable directly on the screen of our oscillograph.

The state of the fiber as modified by the passage of a steady current is generally referred to as the state of *electrotonus*. It has been shown that the electrotonic change of the fiber is brought about by currents passing inwards or outwards through the plasma membrane at the nodes, and not by a current passing through the axis-cylinder. Thus, we use the term *anelectrotonus* to describe the state caused by an inward-directed current and the word *catelectrotonus* for the state caused by a current flowing in the opposite direction.

To obtain experimental data suitable for consideration of nervous transmission along the fiber under electrotonus, we shall now inquire into the electrotonic changes in the threshold as well as in the size of response of an individual node of Ranvier. In the experimental arrangement of Figure 57, top, the circuit labeled P is for application of a steady current to the node under investigation. When the anode of the battery in this circuit is connected directly to the middle electrode, the node N_1 in the

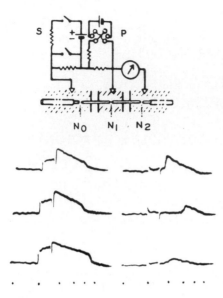

Fig. 57. The effect of electrotonus upon the threshold and action current of a single node of Ranvier. In the diagram on the top, the two lateral pools are filled with a 0.3 per cent cocaine-ringer solution and the node N_1 in the middle is kept in normal ringer; P is the polarizing circuit and S is the stimulating circuit. Polarizing and stimulating voltages used for taking records below are, from right top downwards, 0 mV. and 86 mV., catelectrotonic (c) 100 mV. and 52 mV., c.140 mV. and 75 mV., from left top downwards, anelectrotonic (a) 100 mV. and 360 mV., a. 140 mV. and 480 mV., a. 180 mV. and 620 mV. Time msec. Temperature 18.5°C. (From *Pflügers Arch.*, 246:33.)

middle pool is brought into the state of anelectrotonus. The steady current from this circuit, which is often referred to as a polarizing current, was allowed in the experiment of Figure 57 to flow through the node for a few seconds before a rectangular current pulse from the stimulating circuit R was delivered, and it was withdrawn immediately after a photograph of the action current had been taken. Stimulating pulses were 0.5 millisecond in duration.

As can be seen in the figure, the response of the node is slightly enhanced by anelectrotonus and pronouncedly depressed by catelectrotonus. The threshold is affected by a steady current in such a manner that it is markedly raised by anelectrotonus and slightly reduced by catelectrotonus. The dependence of these quantities upon the strength of the polarizing current is seen in Figure 58, in which the strength of the normal action current is taken, just as in the similar diagrams for the narcotized or refractory nodes, as being equal to 5 times the normal threshold.

2. TRANSMISSION THROUGH AN ELECTROTONIC REGION

Let us send a steady current into a nerve fiber through a pair of electrodes immersed in two pools on both sides of a bridge-

insulator (Fig. 59, top).   Then, one of the two nodes in the immediate neighborhood of the bridge-insulator (N_1 or N_2) is traversed by a steady inward-directed current and is consequently
brought into a state of anelectrotonus, whereas the other one of
them is subjected to a current flowing in the opposite direction
and therefore becomes catelectrotonic.   Our work in this section

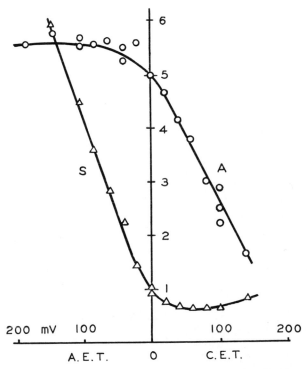

Fig. 58. A graph showing the change in threshold S
and the size of response A of a single node of Ranvier
by electrotonus of varying strengths, derived from
experiment of the preceding figure.   (From *Pflügers
Arch., 246:34*.)

is to investigate the nervous transmission between such nodes
that are in the electrotonic state.

Initiating nerve impulses with the electrodes on the proximal
nerve trunk, we find that the action current of the fiber is
modified by an ascending steady current (namely by a current
entering the fiber in the distal pool and leaving the fiber in the

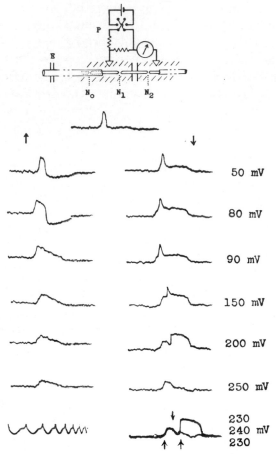

Fig. 59. Change in the configuration of the binodal action currents by ascending (left) and descending (right) polarizing currents of varying strengths. Polarization strengths are given on one side. The last record in the right column shows three sweeps at two different polarization strengths. Time msec. Temperature 16° C. (*Pflügers Arch., 246*:35.)

proximal pool) always in such a manner as can be seen in the records on the left-hand side of Figure 59. With increasing electrotonus strength, the diphasicity of the action current record increases progressively. At a voltage between 70 and 90 millivolts, the diphasic action current changes suddenly into a monophasic one (see the difference between the second and third records in the left column), indicating suspension of transmission at this electrotonus strength. Then, a further increase in electrotonus strength reduces progressively the magnitude of the observed action current.

It is a simple matter to give an interpretation, by virtue of our findings referred to in the last section, to the changes in the configuration of the action currents recorded with ascending steady current. As the upward deflections in these records are indicative of the start of response of the proximal node (N_1 in the figure), it is evident that a steady current which makes this node catelectrotonic should bring about a decrease in the size of the upward deflection. And, since the threshold strength for the distal node N_2 is increased by the steady current, transmission from the proximal to the distal node should be blocked at a certain electrotonus strength.

With the aid of the diagram of Figure 58 in the preceding section, we can roughly estimate the voltage at which transmission between these nodes should be barely suspended. This diagram tells us that the normal action current, the strength of which is 5 in normal threshold units, is reduced by catelectrotonus of about 80 millivolts down to approximately 3 and that, by anelectrotonus of this voltage, the threshold strength is increased from the normal value 1 up to 3. From this it follows that approximately 80 millivolts should be barely sufficient to suspend transmission between these nodes. The actual results are sufficiently concordant to show the legitimacy of our argument.

If, however, the steady current is descending, namely, if the proximal node N_1 is brought into anelectrotonic state and the distal node N_2 into catelectrotonic state, a voltage of 80 millivolts is found to be always insufficient to block the transmission of impulses across this electrotonic region. This experimental fact is simple enough to understand, since the size of response of the proximal node N_1 is increased and the threshold strength for the distal node N_2 is decreased by this steady current. The observed change in the configuration of the action currents is somewhat complicated, as can be seen in the records furnished in the right-hand column of Figure 59. But, in the light of our findings presented in the last section, we easily find a satisfactory interpretation of all these changes.

A weak descending steady current (50 millivolts in the figure) increases the size of the response from the proximal node N_1 and decreases that from the distal node N_2; this changes the configuration of the binodal action current in such a manner that, in the stage during which both N_1 and N_2 are in action, the current arising from N_1 (causing an upward deflection in the electron oscillograph) surmounts the current deriving from N_2, resulting in a prolonged upward deflection of the electron beam during this stage. A stronger steady current lengthens the time required for transmission of impulse from N_0 to N_1, owing to the rise of the threshold strength of the anelectrotonic node N_1; this causes a discontinuity, or a notch, on the ascending limb of the action current record (from 80 to 150 millivolts). In this range of electrotonus strength, the transmission-time from N_1 to N_2 decreases with increasing strength, due evidently to the increase in the ratio of the action current from N_1 to the threshold of N_2; this is doubtless the cause of the shortening of the phase of strong current flow in these records.

If the threshold strength of the node N_1 is increased up to a value five to six times the normal threshold, transmission of impulse from N_0 directly to N_1 should be blocked; but, still the impulse is expected to pass through this region of electrotonus, because the action current developed by the node N_0 is evidently strong enough to excite the distal node N_2. The records with peculiar configuration obtained at 200 and 230 millivolts in the experiment of Figure 59 should be interpreted as being due to progression of excitation from N_0 to N_2 and then to N_1. When both N_0 and N_2 are called into action, the node N_2 in the middle is subjected to a stronger outward-directed current, strong enough to excite this node.

With still stronger steady current (above 240 millivolts in the figure) the node N_1 in the advanced anelectrotonic state is put out of action, owing to its high threshold level. Even at this stage of electrotonus, the impulse jumps from N_0 to N_2 and further to the distal region. Suspension of transmission would occur only when the current is strengthened to such an extent that not only N_1 but also N_0 is put out of action by spread of the steady current. At this strength of electrotonus, the threshold level of the distal node N_2 is no longer lower than the normal value (cathodal depression) and the action current it develops is very small. Actual observation, taking muscular response as the index of transmission, discloses that this occurs when the constant voltage is above approximately 300 millivolts.

It is evident, from what has been stated up to this time, that, if we carry out a similar observation on preparations of which the distal node N_2 in the figure has been rendered inexcitable by narcosis, we should obtain much simpler records than those presented in Figure 59. The records in Figure 60 are those obtained with a descending steady current after introduction of cocaine into the distal pool. As the time required for transmission of impulse from N_0 to N_1 increases with increasing current strength, a notch develops on the ascending limb of the record. The part of the record below the notch derives from the node N_0, but, as soon as the response of N_1 comes into play, the current deriving from N_0 disappears, or *collapses*, and gives way to the action current from the anelectrotonic node N_1, the response of which is slightly larger than that of a normal node. At a certain critical electrotonus strength, the response of the node N_1 suddenly drops out. This sudden change is expected to happen at the voltage at which the threshold of the node N_1 has been raised to about five times the normal value, namely at about 120 millivolts judging by the diagram of Figure 48.

In the year 1934, when the properties of the nodes of Ranvier were first brought to light in Tokyo by an attempt to stimulate excised single fibers with a micro-electrode (Fig. 3 on p. 6), Erlanger and Blair in St. Louis published a paper in which they described the results of experiments substantially the same as those described in this section. These experiments were the first to visualize the discontinuous nature of the nervous transmission in the myelinated fiber (cf. also Blair and Erlanger, 1939).

Quite recently, high frequency impedance measurements were made on single fiber preparations under electrotonus (Tasaki and Mizuguchi, 1949). It was observed that, in the experiment of the type of Figure 60, the response of the node N_1 is always associated with simultaneous loss in the impedance of the system, whereas the response of the node N_0, remote from the bridge-insulator, is unaccompanied by any significant change in the impedance, owing to the leakage of the alternating-bridge current

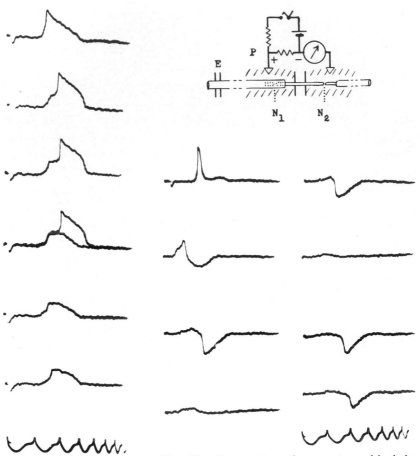

Fig. 60. Similar to Fig. 59, right, but after introduction of a 0.3 per cent cocaine-ringer solution into the distal pool. The polarization strengths in millivolts were, from the top downwards, 0, 100, 110, two sweeps on the same film at 110 and 115, 120 and 150. Time msec. Temperature 17°C. (From *Pflügers Arch., 246: 37.*)

Fig. 61. Restoration of transmission-block by polarization. Left column: From the top downwards, immediately before, 2, 3 and 9.5 minutes after introduction of a 3 per cent urethane-ringer solution into the proximal pool; the polarizing circuit was kept open. Right column: top, 15 sec. after suspension of transmission at polarization strength of 20 mV; 2nd, 1.5 minutes after transmission-block, polarization 0 mV; 3rd and 4th, 2.5 and 5.5 minutes after the block at polarization strength of 50 and 100 mV, respectively. A large motor fiber of the toad, at 20.5°C. (From *Pflügers Arch., 246:38.*)

through the myelin sheath.   For greater detail of these experiments one may refer to the original article.

3.   RESTORATION OF TRANSMISSION BY ELECTROTONUS

We have seen before that, in narcosis of a short stretch of a nerve fiber, suspension of transmission takes place when the action current derived from the narcotized region falls short of the threshold level of the distal normal node.   We now know that it is possible to reduce the threshold of a node to a considerable degree by passage of a steady current.   It follows from this that we should be able to restore transmission, once suspended by narcosis, by the use of a steady current.   In this section, we are concerned with a simple experiment showing that this actually occurs.

The arrangement used for the experiment and an example of the results obtained are given in Figure 61.   With the polarizing circuit P in the figure kept open, application of a 3 per cent urethane-ringer solution on the portion of the single fiber preparation in the proximal (left) pool changed the configuration of the observed action current as shown by the records in the left-hand column.   This is the change with which we are fully acquainted from the explanation of the experiment of Figure 51 on p. 96.   We know that, immediately before suspension of transmission, a record is obtained showing the response of the distal node starting towards the end of the response from the narcotized region.   Soon after such a record is obtained, there occurs a sudden change in the observed action current, indicating a complete disappearance of the response of the distal node.

Immediately following suspension of transmission the circuit P in the figure was closed and a constant voltage of about 10 millivolts was applied to the fiber.   Under these circumstances, delivery of an induction shock to the proximal nerve trunk was found to yield an action current showing that the distal node N_2 had now been called into action.   As time elapsed, the constant voltage required for the restoration of transmission increased progressively; this in turn decreased the magnitude of the response of the distal node.

Such an effect of a constant voltage upon the transmission block was first described by Woronzow (1924) who worked on frogs'

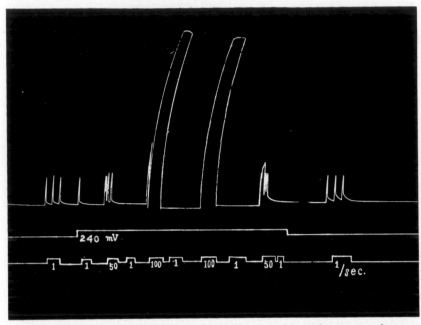

Fig. 62. Facilitation of Erlanger and Blair observed by taking muscular contraction as index of transmission.   A motor nerve fiber-sartorius muscle
preparation of the toad.   The signal at the bottom shows delivery of repetitive
induction shocks to the proximal nerve trunk; the frequencies of shocks are
given. The upper signal indicates application of a steady descending current
(caused by a constant voltage of 240 mV) to the operated region of the
preparation.

nerve-muscle preparations.   In 1937, Hodgkin carried out a very
important experiment in which he showed that cold or compression block of nerve could readily be restored by a brief current pulse so timed as to act upon the distal side of the blocked
region concurrently with the action current.   Unlike constant currents, a brief current pulse reduces the threshold for a brief period
after delivery.   Mapping out the time-course of the minimum
strength of current required for restoration of transmission, Hodgkin brought out the first clear-cut demonstration of the decisive
role of the action current in nervous transmission.

4.   THE FACILITATION OF ERLANGER AND BLAIR

Erlanger and Blair (1939, 1940) discovered an interesting
phenomenon on nerve fibers under electrotonus.   They found that

the anelectrotonic transmission-block can be temporarily over-come by the arrival of several impulses at the region of blockade. This phenomenon seems, as Erlanger (1939) himself stresses, to provide a means of approaching the mechanism responsible for facilitation in the central nervous system. We shall make mention in this section of several experiments undertaken to confirm, with excised single nerve fibers, what has been discovered by Erlanger and Blair.

For the experiment of Figure 62, a nerve fiber-muscle preparation was used. To the muscle of this preparation was attached a lever to register muscular contraction on a smoked drum. When induction shocks were delivered to the proximal nerve trunk of this preparation at a frequency of 1 per second, twitches of the muscle were found to recur at the same rate as the applied stimulus. The three twitches seen on the left end of the figure are the ones thus induced. Then, a constant voltage of 240 millivolts was applied to the operated region of the preparation (which was laid on a bridge-insulator) to cause a steady current in the descending direction. The start of this current induced in the muscle a twitch; but, all during the passage of this current, induction shocks delivered to the proximal nerve trunk at a low frequency failed to elicit twitches in the muscle. All the impulses arriving at the electrotonic region after long intervals were blocked.

When, however, the frequency of the shocks was raised up to 50 per second in this state of electrotonus, the muscle gave rise to an incomplete tetanic contraction. Furthermore, shocks of 100 per second were found to give a complete tetanus. It is evident that under these circumstances several blocked impulses facilitate transmission of the following impulses. The facilitation of transmission of this type can very readily be observed whenever the strength of the polarizing current is only barely sufficient to block transmission.

It is also easy to demonstrate the facilitation of Erlanger and Blair with an oscillograph used in conjunction with an amplifier. In the experiment of Figure 63, the portion of the single fiber preparation in the distal pool was treated with cocaine and was rendered inexcitable. It is shown in the figure that, at an appropriate strength of the steady polarizing current, the second impulse travels as far as the node N_1 whereas the first impulse is blocked between N_0 and N_1. Although the experimental condition in this observation is not the same as that for the experiment of Figure 62, it is clear that the underlying process is common to the two cases.

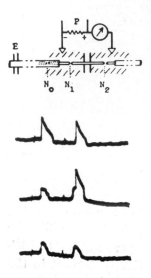

Let us now consider the mechanism of this phenomenon. When a nerve impulse arrives at node N_0 in Figure 63, the node N_1 which has been traversed by a steady inward-directed current is subjected to a strong outward-directed current for a short period. This naturally tends to bring the latter node from the anelectrotonic state towards the normal. Thus the threshold for the node N_1 is temporarily lowered by a blocked impulse, but, as time elapses, the node N_1 returns gradually to the original analectrotonic state. As we shall see in the following section, the development of the electrotonic state is a relatively slow process, so slow that several blocked impulses can bring about a summative effect. The impulse which arrives at the node N_1 when the threshold of this node has been lowered to some extent brings this node into action. It may therefore be concluded that the facilitation we have observed above is due to the threshold-lowering effect of the blocked impulses.

Fig. 63. The uppermost record: Action currents observed after introduction of a 0.3 per cent cocaine-ringer solution into the distal pool. Middle: The effect of a constant voltage of 130 mV. Bottom: 135 mV. A motor nerve fiber of the toad, at 15°C. The interval between the two shocks, 6.5 msec.

5. DEVELOPMENT OF THE ELECTROTONIC STATE

We are concerned in this section with the consideration of how fast the electrotonic state develops under action of a steady current traversing through a node of Ranvier. We have seen that the catelectrotonus reduces the strength of the action current of the node to a considerable extent. It is therefore desirable to determine the rate at which this change progresses under the influence of a constant current. But it is not feasible to do this,

as a constant current of a suprarheobasic strength sets up by itself
a response and throws the node into refractoriness in the period
during which the catelectrotonic change is expected to progress.
We shall therefore examine how fast the catelectrotonic change
of the action current disappears when the steady current has been
cut off.

In the experiment of Figure 64, left, a single node of Ranvier
which had been isolated functionally by narcosis of the neighboring nodes was subjected to a strong outward-directed current
(caused by a constant voltage of 100 millivolts) for a period of
about one second.   Towards the end of this constant current

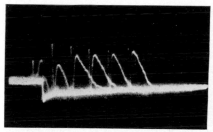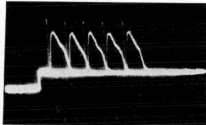

Fig. 64. Recovery of height of response and the threshold after the end of
catelectrotonus (left) and anelectrotonus (right) of 100 mV. The arrangement used was similar to that shown in Figure 57, top, but an induction coil
was employed in place of the stimulating circuit for generating rectangular
current pulses. All the stimuli were of the threshold strength at that moment.
Six or five sweeps were superposed on the same photographic film.   Induction shocks were shifted at interval of 1 msec.   A large motor fiber of the
toad at 23.5°C.

pulse, a single induction shock was delivered to the node, and a
record was taken of the action current released by a shock of
threshold strength.   Then the position of the shock relative to
the end of the polarizing current was changed and similar observations were made.   The record on the left-hand side of Figure 64
was taken by superposing six sweeps on the same film.   In this
example, the position of the induction shock was shifted by incre-
ments of 1 millisecond.   It is seen in this figure that the size of
response and the threshold strength (seen from the size of shock-
artefact) approaches normal relatively quickly after the end of
the polarizing current.   Attention should be called in this experiment to the fact that, following the removal of the polarizing

current, the threshold of the node shows a value much higher than that for a normal node. As the size of the response recovers gradually after withdrawal of the polarizing current, the threshold approaches normal with equal pace.

The record on the right-hand side of Figure 64 is the one obtained from the same node on removal of anelectrotonus of the same strength. Here again, the threshold for the node is higher in the post-anelectrotonic state than in the normal (cf. Tasaki, 1950a). As can be seen in the figure, there are still considerable differences both in the form of action current and in the threshold strength between the two last responses in the right- and left-hand photographs. It is therefore evident that a much longer time is required for a complete recovery from the effect of electrotonus.

CHAPTER IX

THE NERVE TRUNK

I. PROPERTIES OF SMALL MYELINATED NERVE FIBERS

We shall begin this chapter by describing some general properties of small myelinated nerve fibers which are found in
abundance in the nerve trunk. There is an extensive literature
dealing with the relationship between the rate of transmission and
the diameter of the myelinated nerve fiber (Gasser and Erlanger,
1927; Bishop and Heinbecker, 1930; Blair and Erlanger, 1936;
Gasser and Erlanger, 1936; Zotterman, 1937; Hursh, 1939; Gasser
and Grundfest, 1939; etc.). We shall here describe the results
of measurements made with isolated single nerve fibers (Tasaki,
Ishii and Ito, 1943).

In Figure 65 are collected the data from 49 single fiber preparations of the bull frog at 24°C. It is seen in this figure that the
transmission-rate falls off linearly with the fiber-diameter. At a
given fiber-diameter, however, there is a wide variation in the
transmission-rate. It appears probable that this wide variation
is at least in part due to the non-uniformity of the fiber-diameter
along the course of individual fibers, which we sometimes notice
in nerve fibers exposed for a length including several internodal
segments.

It was found by the method of average equation applied to
the data of Figure 65 that the statistical relation between the
transmission-rate V in meters per second and the fiber-diameter
D in microns can be expressed by the formula

$$V = 2.05D,$$

the correlation coefficient between the two being 0.92.

The data collected in Figure 66 shows that the threshold (for
induction currents) also varies as the fiber-diameter. The
threshold strengths were measured with a pair of platinum electrodes of the interpolar length of 2.5 millimeters placed on the
sciatic nerve of the bull frog. The stimulating currents were from

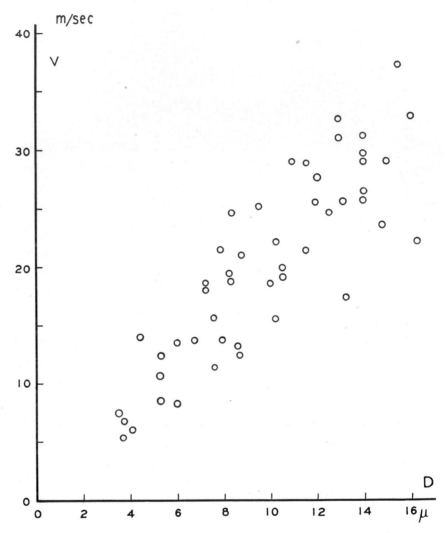

Fig. 65. Transmission-rate of individual nerve fibers V plotted against fiber-diameter D. Sciatic-gastrocnemius preparations of the bull frog. The outside-diameter of the fiber was measured at the operated region near the muscle. The transmission-rate was determined by the method described in Chapter III. Temperature 24°C. (From *Japan. J. Med. Sc., III; Biophysics,* 9:193.)

an inductorium of which the secondary coil had a self-inductance of 0.1 henry. It is seen in this figure that the threshold strength increases remarkably with decreasing fiber-diameter.

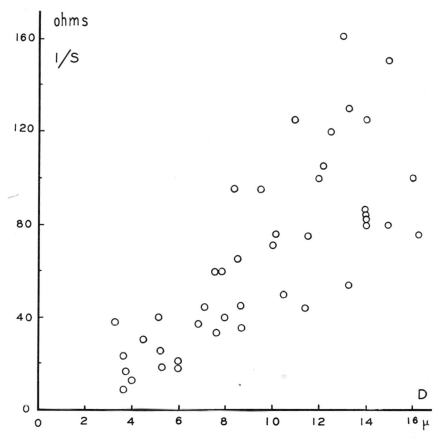

Fig. 66. Reciprocal of the threshold strength S plotted against the fiber-diameter D. Single fibers of the bull frog. (From *Japan. J. Med. Sci., III; Biophysics,* 9:194.)

The next figure (Fig. 67) shows the relationship between the internodal distance and the fiber-diameter. As has been pointed out by a number of previous investigators, the internodal distance L is seen to increase in parallel with the diameter of the fiber D, the relation between the two being given by the formula

$$L = 0.146 \times 10^3 D$$

The correlation coefficient between L and D was found, from these data, to be 0.62.

As the cross-section area of nerve fibers varies as the diameter

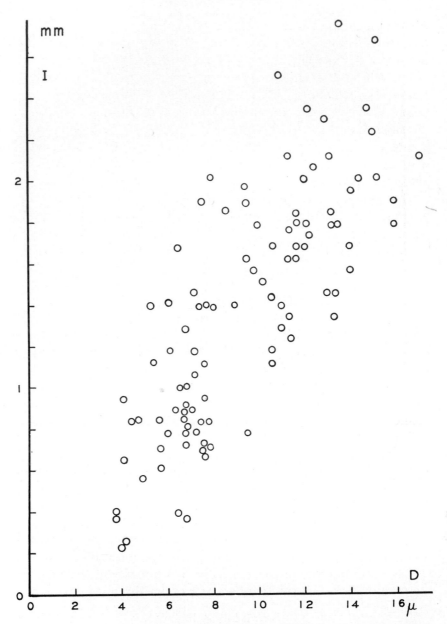

Fig. 67. Internodal distance I plotted against fiber-diameter D.   Data from
100 fibers of the bull frog.   (From *Japan. J. Med. Sc., III; Biophysics,*
9:195.)

squared, it follows from the linear relationship between L and D that the resistance of the axis-cylinder between the two neighboring nodes of Ranvier should vary inversely as the fiber-diameter. If, therefore, the action-e.m.f. developed at the plasma membrane at the node is constant regardless of the fiber-type, the amplitude of the binodal action current should vary directly as the fiber-diameter. And the results of all the previous experiments with intact nerve preparations and of direct observations with excised single fibers agree in showing a linear relation between the spike-height of the action current and the fiber-diameter.

The average internodal transmission-time T is obtained by dividing the internodal distance L by the transmission-rate V. Since both L and V are shown to be proportional to the fiber-diameter D, the ratio L/V is independent of D; namely, for the data shown in the figures,

$$T = \frac{L}{V} = 0.071 \ (\text{msec.}).$$

This undoubtedly signifies that in saltatory transmission every node of Ranvier is brought into action by the current developed by the neighboring node, with a latency of 0.07 millisecond. It is known however that the internodal transmission-time for young regenerating nerve fibers is shorter than that for the adult ones (Sanders and Whitteridge, 1946).

Smaller fibers show a definite tendency to develop longer action currents and to possess longer absolutely refractory periods. But, when we compare the entire course of recovery curve for a small fiber with that for a large one, we frequently find that the relatively refractory periods are not much different between the two. As has been pointed out by Erlanger, Gasser and Bishop (1927), the rate of recovery does not seem to vary appreciably as the fiber-diameter.

2. MULTI-FIBER PREPARATION

When we tease a bundle of nerve fibers with sharp needles, we see many fine fibers along which no node of Ranvier is discernible. These unmyelinated fibers are frequently found to form special bundles sometimes together with some small myelinated fibers (see the micro-photographs in Fig. 68). The properties

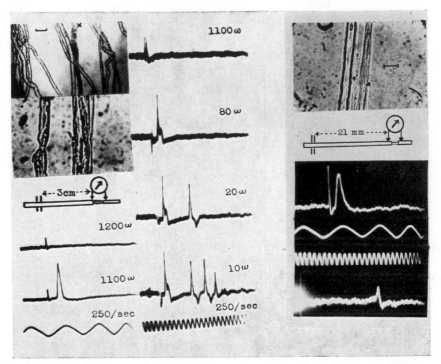

Fig. 68. Left: The microphotograph at the top shows a stage in an operation to isolate a bundle consisting mainly of unmyelinated fibers in a toad's skin nerve. The bar subtends 50 microns. The bundle is marked by the cross. All the fibers except this bundle and a large myelinated fiber were cut across and another photograph was taken at a magnification five times as high as in the first picture. The following action current records were taken from this preparation. Records on the right column were taken at a lower transit speed and a higher (twice) amplification. The reciprocal of the strength of the induction shock is given. Temperature 28°C. (From *J. Physiol. 117*:136.)

Right: A large myelinated nerve fiber and a group of unmyelinated fibers isolated from a muscle nerve of the toad and their action currents. The bar in the micro-photograph subtends 20 microns. The uppermost action current record was taken at a high transit speed. The lowermost record was obtained with an induction shock about 80 times as strong as that in the uppermost record. The transit speed in this case is so low, as can be seen from the time signal of 250 cycles per sec. in the middle, the action current from the large myelinated fiber, together with the shock-artefact, is seen as a faint straight line on the left. 28°C. (From *J. Physiol., 117*:161.)

of these fibers have hitherto been investigated only with intact nerve trunks (Erlanger and Gasser, 1930; Bishop, 1934–35; Richard and Gasser, 1935; and others) or with multi-fiber preparations (Fig. 68). The transmission along these unmyelinated fibers is very slow (1 to 0.1 meter per second at room temperature) and is probably continuous, and not saltatory, since they have no nodes of Ranvier. Their threshold for induction shocks (applied through electrodes placed on the intact nerve trunk) is very high (at least 100 to 200 times the threshold for the largest myelinated fibers). The action currents from these fibers are very slow and feeble.

With multi-fiber preparations, it is easily disclosed that the fibers in the preparation transmit impulses practically independent of one another (see Fig. 69). Under normal experimental conditions, the rate of transmission in each fiber is not affected at all by whether or not the surrounding fibers are in action. It has been shown that potassium chloride (Hodgkin and Huxley, 1947), thiamine (von Muralt, 1945) and possibly acetylcholine (see Fulton and Nachmansohn, 1943), besides metabolic products (see Gerard, 1932), are liberated from the nerve fiber in action. But all the interactions of neighboring fibers which have hitherto been demonstrated for the vertebrate nerve seem to be electrical in nature (see Marrazzi and Lorente de Nó, 1944).

There is no doubt that every node of Ranvier of active fibers in a nerve trunk behaves as the source of current of the temporal configuration shown in Figure 30 (p. 62). The field of potential generated by all these sources should affect the resting fibers in such a manner as can be inferred from the experiments of Figures 3 (p. 6) and 34 (p. 70). But such an interaction is under normal experimental conditions very slight.

3. ACTION POTENTIAL LED FROM THE SURFACE OF THE NERVE TRUNK

We shall now consider the time course of the potential difference between two points on the surface of a nerve trunk induced by an impulse traveling along a single fiber in the nerve. The simplest case to be considered is the potential difference between the two points at a distance less than one internodal length apart. Let us assume that there exists no node of Ranvier of the fiber in the portion of the nerve under consideration. Then, it is evident that an action current of the ordinary binodal configuration flows through the portion of nerve when the single fiber transmits an impulse. The time course of the potential difference between these two points, therefore, should be given by the product of the strength of a binodal action current by the resistance of the surrounding medium of the fiber between these two points. As

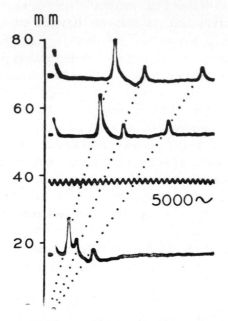

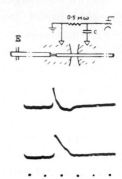

Fig. 69. Records of action currents taken from a three-fiber preparation at three different transmission-distances. The sciatic-tibial nerve of the toad at 22°C. The diameters of the fibers were 13, 9 and 5 microns. The strength of the induction shock employed was twice the threshold for the smallest fiber.

Fig. 70. The time course of the action potential obtained with the arrangement shown by the diagram on the top. The lower record was obtained after application of a 0.3 per cent cocaine-ringer solution to the portion of the nerve in the distal pool. Time msec.; temperature 20°C. (From *J. Neurophysiol., 11*:300.)

the resistance of the single fiber is far greater than that of the medium, the resistance of the medium between the two points is practically equal to the resistance of the whole nerve between the two points.

The upper oscillograph record furnished in Figure 70 shows the configuration of the action potential taken with the arrangement illustrated by the diagram in this figure. The slender unoperated portion of single fiber preparation was laid across a bridge-insulator. The portion of the nerve suspended in the air gap was about 0.5 millimeter in length. It is seen that the potential difference between the two pools induced by a nerve impulse traveling along a single nerve fiber actually shows the ordinary binodal configuration. From this we may infer that the single fiber under investigation had no node of Ranvier in the portion of the nerve between the two pools of ringer. Introduction of cocaine into the distal pool changed the configuration just as in the experiment with the isolated region of the fiber mounted on the bridge-insulator (compare the records in Fig. 70 with those in Fig. 15 on p. 38).

With this experimental arrangement, it was actually found that the amplitude of the observed action potential varied as the resistance of the nerve between the two pools. Action potentials of as large as 100 microvolts are observed only when the resistance is about 50 kilohms or a little more. The strength of the action current as determined by dividing the observed potential by the resistance was found, in a series of experiments made with single motor fibers innervating the sartorius muscle of the toad at about 20°C, to be consistently between 1.3 and 2×10^{-9} ampere. This value agrees well, though not very accurately, with the strength of action current obtained with the operated region of single fiber preparation mounted on the bridge-insulator.

4. THE MONOPHASIC ACTION POTENTIAL

We are now prepared to derive the configuration of the potential obtainable by the so-called monophasic lead from the configurations of the action currents so far described. Let us suppose that in the diagram of Figure 71 the nodes of Ranvier N_3 and N_4 have been rendered inexcitable with cocaine and other nodes N_0, N_1 and N_2 are in the normal state. Let us assume further that the nerve trunk containing this fiber has a uniform diameter and is kept in the air. Then, it is evident from what has been stated in the preceding section that a nerve impulse traveling downwards along the single fiber shown in the diagram induces, between the two points on the nodes N_0 and N_1, a potential difference having a typical binodal configuration. Similarly, the configuration of the potential difference between the two points on the nerve just outside the nodes N_1 and N_2 should be binodal; but the start of this potential should lag behind that of the action potential taken between N_0 and N_1 by an internodal transmission-time.

The potential difference on the nerve between the two points on N_2 and N_3 in the figure, however, must be of a triangular configuration, because N_3 and all other nodes which follow N_3 are

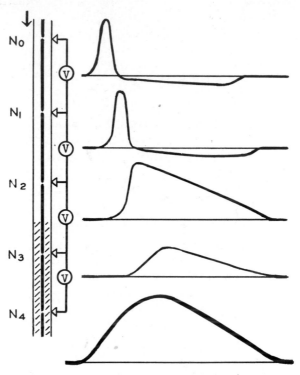

Fig. 71. Reconstruction of monophasic action potential of single fiber preparation. The thin curves represent the potential differences between the nodes and the thick curve the sum of these four curves.

supposed to be treated with cocaine. Furthermore, there should result between N_3 and N_4 a potential difference of a round configuration, since we have seen in the experiment of Figure 20 on p. 45 that an action current suffers a considerable reduction in its early part as it spreads beyond a completely narcotized node.

Now, the action potential led from this nerve with a pair of electrodes placed one on the node N_0 and the other on N_4 should naturally be given by the algebraic sum of all the potential differences between the four internodal segments of the nerve. This yields, as can be seen in the figure, a potential curve resembling the typical monophasic spike-potential from a single fiber recorded by previous investigators (e.g. Gasser and Erlanger, 1936, Figs. 42, 57, 78 etc.).* Under the conditions of ordinary experiments with nerve trunk, however, the positions of the nodes of Ranvier relative to the lead electrodes remain unknown to us.

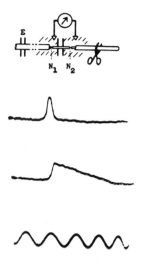

Another procedure of leading monophasic action potentials from a single nerve fiber in a nerve trunk is crushing the nerve between the two lead electrodes, instead of applying a narcotic upon the nerve on the distal electrode. We shall, therefore, digress for a moment to describe the effect of cutting a nerve fiber upon the configuration of the action currents.

When a single motor nerve fiber of the toad laid on a bridge-insulator is cut across at a point 0.5 to 3 millimeters distal to the bridge-insulator (Fig. 72), it is found that the binodal action current changes immediately into a triangular one, as can be seen in the figure. If the distance between the bridge-insulator and the site of cutting is 2 to 3 millimeters, the excitability of the distal node in the figure recovers gradually during the course of about 30 minutes and the observed action current becomes grad-

Fig. 72. The upper record: A binodal action current taken from a normal motor nerve fiber of the toad. The lower record: Action current observed after cutting the nerve at a point 2.5 mm. distant from the bridge-insulator. Time marker, 1000 cycles per sec. Temperature 11.5°C.

ually diphasic. In cases where the distance is above 8 millimeters, the binodal action current remains almost unchanged for a long time. When a cut is given to the fiber immediately below the

---

* Erlanger seems to believe that the monophasic action potential from a single nerve fiber is composed of a small number of nodal components. We can not however regard the action potential as such, because the change in the resistance of the nodal plasma membrane during activity makes a formal application of the principle of superposition to this system impossible (see Fig. 24 on p. 53).

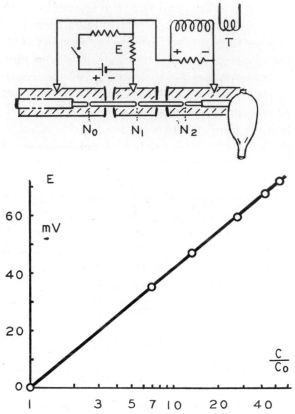

Fig. 73. Measurement of the "salt potential" by the method of threshold reduction. With the two lateral pools filled with normal ringer, the fluid in the middle pool was replaced with mixtures of an isotonic KCl solution and the normal ringer at varying ratio. As the threshold for the distal node N_2 was reduced by this procedure, a constant voltage was applied to the portion of the fiber in the middle pool and the voltage E required for bringing back the threshold of the node N_2 to normal was determined. In the lower graph, the ratio of the KCl content of the fluid in the middle pool to that of the normal ringer (0.015 per cent) was plotted as abscissa on the logarithmic scale. (From Tasaki, 1944.)

bridge-insulator, it is observed that the triangular action current deriving from the proximal node N_1 suffers a considerable reduction in its spike-height, due apparently to the effect of the so-called injury current making N_1 catelectronic. We now clearly understand how an interruption, by crushing, of the continuity of a nerve fiber between the two lead electrodes changes the configuration of the action potential from the fiber.

Application of an isotonic KCl solution is also a procedure often used to make the action potential monophasic. The effects of this solution upon the node of Ranvier are (1) suppression of action current production, (2) generation of a constant current which makes the neighboring nodes catelectrotonic (see Fig. 73) and (3) reduction of the resistance through the nodal plasma membrane. The change in the resistance to the current traversing the nodal plasma membrane has been demonstrated by measuring the spread of current beyond the region treated with KCl after compensation of the "salt-potential." These results are consistent with those obtained by Hodgkin (1947) for invertebrate nerve fibers.

A nerve of which the action potential has been made monophasic is in a somewhat unstable state. If one end of a nerve has been treated with KCl, for instance, the normal region of the nerve near the KCl-treated end becomes progressively abnormal, due to diffusion of KCl along the nerve. We have already seen that after mechanical injury the condition of the fiber changes gradually. It is sometimes dangerous, therefore, to attribute great significance to the shape of the monophasic action potential.

The monophasic action potential led from a whole nerve trunk is given by summation of all the action potentials arising from the constituent fibers. As has been stated in the early part of this chapter, smaller fibers develop smaller action potentials which arrive at the position of the lead electrodes after longer shock-response intervals. The fiber-size distribution in the peripheral nerve is not simple but it shows several peaks of numerical predominance. In accordance with this fact, the monophasic action potential led from a whole nerve trunk shows a small number of separate elevations. For a greater detail of the work along this line, one may refer to the well known book written by Erlanger and Gasser (1937).

5.   THE DIPHASIC ACTION POTENTIAL

We shall now consider the distribution of potential on the surface of an intact nerve caused by an impulse traveling along a
single fiber in the nerve.   Let us assume that the property of the
preparation is such that a nerve fiber with a constant internodal

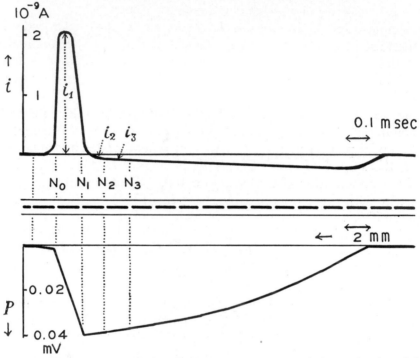

Fig. 74. Construction of the diphasic action potential from the binodal
action current of a single nerve fiber by virtue of Ohm's law.   The maximum
height of the binodal action current is assumed to be 2×10^{-9} ampere, its
duration to be 1.2 msec., the rate of transmission to be 24 m./sec., the internodal length of the fiber to be 2 mm. and the resistance of the nerve trunk
to be 10^5 ohms per cm.   (From *Pflügers Arch.*, 245:780.)

length generates binodal action currents of a given strength all
along the fiber (Fig. 74).   We shall suppose, contrary to our habit
in this book, the impulse to travel from the right end of the nerve
leftwards.

At the moment when the binodal action current flowing between the nodes N_0 and N_1 has just attained the maximum, the
current through the nerve (outside the fiber under consideration)

is considered to follow the spacial distribution shown by the upper diagram in this figure. This is the configuration of an ordinary binodal action current of which the time-axis is converted into a length-axis by the relation (an internodal transmission-time) → (an internodal length).[*]

In this diagram, the current through the medium between the resting node N_0 and the node N_1 brought into action latest is denoted by i_1. As this current is directed from N_0 towards N_1 in the medium, this naturally lowers the potential at the point just outside N_1 relative to N_0, the potential difference being given by the product of this current by the resistance of the medium between N_0 and N_1. Thus, the distribution of potentials on the nerve between N_0 and N_1 is given by the corresponding straight line in the lowermost diagram. If the leakage of current through the myelin sheath is taken into consideration in this case, the potential along the nerve between N_0 and N_1 should be represented by a smooth curve instead of a straight line in the figure.

In an entirely analogous manner, the distribution of potential along the stretch of the nerve between N_1 and N_2 is constructed by formal application of Ohm's law to the medium surrounding the fiber. The lowermost diagram in Figure 73 shows the distribution of potential, thus constructed, along a nerve which contains a single fiber carrying an impulse. As the impulse progresses, the wave of potential thus generated travels along the nerve at the rate of transmission of the impulse. In the so-called diphasic lead of action potential, we record the difference between the potentials at two points on an intact nerve resulting from the wave of potential figured out above.

The question now arises: Is the potential in the resting region of a nerve behind an active region equal to the potential in the resting part in front of the active region? The answer to this question is more complicated than it may appear at first sight.

We employ in this consideration the following notations:

$U(x)$, the potential at the point x on the nerve trunk, the variable x representing the length measured along the length-axis of the nerve;

---

[*] If one denotes the strength of the current flowing through the medium at the middle of the n-th internodal segment at time t by $i_n(t)$, it is evident that in this system $i_{n+1}(t - \Delta t) = i_n(t)$, where Δt represents the internodal transmission-time.

$V(x)$,   the potential in the axis-cylinder inside the nerve fiber un-
          der consideration at the distance x;

W,   the resistance per unit length of the axis-cylinder of the
          fiber;

w,   the resistance per unit length of the nerve;

E,   the potential difference existing between the medium and
          the axis-cylinder in the resting region of the fiber.

We disregard the wave-like path of the nerve fiber within the
nerve trunk and regard all the (resting and action) electromotive
forces as located at the boundary between the medium and the
axis-cylinder. Under these circumstances, it is evident that the
current flowing through the conducting medium in the nerve is of
equal strength (but with the opposite sign) as the current traversing the axis-cylinder at that point, no matter what the distribution
of the electromotive force at the membrane may be. This can be
expressed by the differential equation

$$- \frac{1}{w} \frac{dU(x)}{dx} = \frac{1}{W} \frac{dV(x)}{dx}. \qquad (1)$$

In case where the ratio W/w is constant throughout the stretch
of the nerve under consideration, we obtain by integration

$$- \frac{W}{w} U(x) = V(x) + C, \qquad (2)$$

where C is the integration constant.

In the resting region of the nerve fiber where there is no current
through the boundary between the axis-cylinder and the medium,
the potential in- and outside the fiber should differ only by the
resting membrane-e.m.f. E. Denoting the position of the two
resting points of the fiber on both sides of an active region by
$x = a$ and $x = b$, we have relations

$$V(a) = U(a) - E,$$

and

$$V(b) = U(b) - E.$$

From equation (2), we find also that

$$- \frac{W}{w} U(a) = V(a) + C,$$

and

$$- \frac{W}{w} U(b) = V(b) + C.$$

loss of impedance of the surface membrane of the squid giant axon during activity. Further, Katz and Schmitt (1940) observed interactions of an electric nature between two unmyelinated nerve fibers lying close to each other.

The results of direct measurements of action potentials across the surface membrane of the squid giant axon, conducted by Hodgkin and Huxley (1939 and 1945) and by Curtis and Cole (1940), are also of great importance in the consideration of the mechanism of transmission in the unmyelinated fiber. But, as the author of this book has had no experience in the experimental study of unmyelinated fibers, it would be safer for us not to go into the details of these beautiful works. And, here, we shall discuss only about what kind of modification we have to introduce into our picture of the nerve impulse if we take the structural features of the unmyelinated fiber into consideration.

It is well-known that the distribution of a steady current in the extra-polar region of an unmyelinated fiber is given by the formula

$$i(x) = i_o e^{-x/\lambda}.$$

Here, the function $i(x)$ denotes the strength of the current flowing through the surface membrane of the fiber at distance x along the fiber from the electrode and λ represents a constant with the dimension of length characterizing the electric structure of the fiber. We have seen already that the corresponding equation for the myelinated fiber is

$$i_n = i_o e^{-n/\mu}$$

(equation 1, on p. 30, with new notations introduced by the relations $i_o = E/r$ and $e^{-1/\mu} = a$). In the unmyelinated fiber, the spread of current is described by a continuous exponential function while in the myelinated fiber it is given by a discontinuous function. On this ground, one might consider an unmyelinated fiber to be a system attainable by letting the internodal distance of a myelinated fiber approach zero. But the situation is not so simple as it may appear at first sight.

In the myelinated fiber, the gap between the myelin sheath at the nodes of Ranvier is very narrow, being in most cases less than 1 micron. Staempfli (personal communication) estimated the area of the plasma membrane at the node of the frog motor fiber to be about 2×10^{-7} cm^2. As the resistance of this membrane to the penetrating current is known to be about 50 megohms or slightly more (see p. 146), it follows that the resistance of this membrane per unit area is of the order of 10 ohm $\cdot$ cm^2 or slightly more. This figure is far smaller than the resistance of the surface membrane of the actual unmyelinated fiber; the value obtained by Cole and Hodgkin (1939) for the squid giant axon is 0.3 to 1×10^3 ohm $\cdot$ cm^2. If a long cylinder of protoplasm were covered with a membrane of the resistance of only few ohms per unit area, then the space constant λ for the system would become very small and, as a consequence, the rate of transmission of impulses along such a system would become far lower than that of the actual unmyelinated fiber. This is the reason why we can not regard an unmyelinated fiber simply as a system obtainable by reducing the internodal distance of a myelinated fiber to zero.

Huxley and Stämpfli (1949) estimated the resistance of the myelin sheath of the frog motor fiber to be of the order of 10^5 ohm $\cdot$ cm^2. It is clear from these results that the surface membrane of the squid giant axon has still very low resistance as compared with the myelin sheath.

The capacity of the myelin sheath estimated by Huxley and Stämpfli (1949) is of the order of 2×10^{-9} farad/cm^2. The capacity of the plasma membrane at the node of Ranvier seems to be of the order of 10^{-5} farad/cm^2. The corresponding value for the squid giant axon is, according to Hodgkin and Rushton (1946), approximately 10^{-6} farad/cm^2.

Although all these estimates of the electrical constants of the myelinated fiber are of somewhat indirect nature, their results are probably not far from the truth. And the figures obtained from these estimates give us some ideas about the differences between myelinated and unmyelinated fibers.

APPENDIX I

TECHNIQUE OF PREPARING A SINGLE
VERTEBRATE NERVE FIBER

The technique of isolating a single motor nerve fiber entering the frog gastrocnemius has been described elsewhere (Kato, 1934; Tasaki, 1939a). Recently, Huxley and Staempfli (1949) improved the method of illumination and the technique of obtaining a long single fiber preparation. The following method of preparation can be applied to many kinds of nerve from cold and warm blooded animals.

MICROSCOPE AND ILLUMINATION

As the size of a vertebrate nerve fiber (0.1 to 20 microns diameter) is far below our visual acuity, it is necessary to use a binocular microscope for dissection. Magnification of 5 to 20 times seems adequate. Under a microscope of higher magnification, free hand dissection becomes difficult.

Since the magnification of the microscope available is thus limited, it becomes necessary to make nerve fibers well visible by means of dark field illumination. Adrian and Bronk (1928), as well as Shimizu (see Kato, 1934), obtained a dark field by placing a transparent glass-plate, carrying the nerve, on a black object and illuminating the nerve from above. The present author had obtained a dark field by illuminating the nerve from beneath by cones of light which did not enter directly into the binocular microscope. Huxley uses a large dark-field condenser fixed under an ordinary dissecting binocular microscope.

INSTRUMENTS USED FOR OPERATION

The main tools used for the operation are needles fixed rigidly to holders made of electrical insulator. Ordinary sewing needles, sharpened on a whetstone, are serviceable. Sharpness and flexibility of the needles suited for the operation vary according to the stage of the operation (see below). The shape of the sharp-

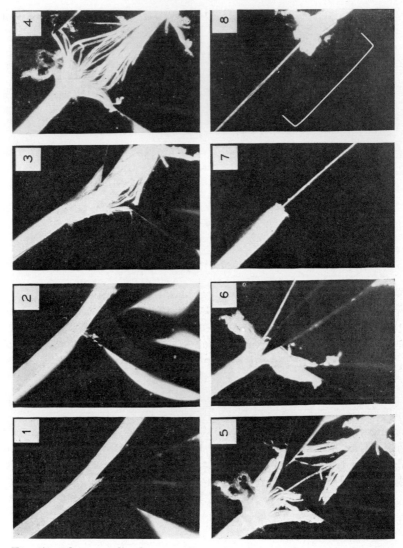

Fig. 76. Photographs showing the operation to isolate a single nerve fiber from a slender nerve without branching. The nerve innervating the simitendinosus and sartorius muscles of the frog was used. The contours of the needles are seen faintly in the pictures. These photographs were taken at Cambridge with the arrangements and camera which Mr. A. F. Huxley has kindly lent to the author.

ened needle-tip (whether simply conical or edged) does not matter a great deal, because the tips of the needles are mainly used for cutting and teasing the nerve fibers.

For the operation on a large nerve trunk, Staempfli's scissors are very useful; one of the blades of these scissors is slightly longer than the other blade, and the connective-tissue sheath of the nerve can readily be severed with them, keeping the longer blade inside the nerve trunk.

A squirt and a painting brush are serviceable for changing the fluid around the preparation.

POSTURE OF OPERATOR

In order to minimize the tremor of the tip of the needle held by the operator, it is highly desirable to lay the operator's elbows on the table and the hands on the platform where the nerve is placed. It is also necessary to grip the holder as close to the needle as possible and make the tips of the middle, ring and small fingers rest on the glass-plate where the preparation is laid. The height of the table and the chair also affect the stability of the operator's hands. The present author usually places the binocular microscope at such a position on the table that his breast lightly touches the edge of the table.

PROCEDURE OF OPERATION

Figure 76 shows the procedure of operation on a small nerve without branching. The operation on a large nerve or a small nerve branching from a relatively large nerve can be done more readily than this in almost the same manner (see Tasaki, 1939a).

The first step of the operation is to make a small hole in the connective tissue sheath which surrounds the nerve fibers by cutting the sheath with a sharp needle (see photograph 1, Fig. 76). Then the tip of the needle is inserted into the nerve through this hole in the direction parallel to the nerve fibers, and a small part of the connective-tissue sheath is split by pressing the glass-plate with the tip of the needle. Repeating this procedure (2), a large opening is made on one side of the nerve sheath. Next, the sheath is pulled out on the other side and is cut across (3). Care should be taken in this case not to leave a part of the sheath uncut. Under dark-field illumination, the connective-tissue sheath looks distinctly less bright and more homogeneous than the nerve fibers.

Then, with more or less blunt needles, the bundle of nerve fibers is split in such a way that some of the intact nerve fibers are separated from one another in the middle (4). This procedure turns out to be unsuccessful if a part of the connective tissue sheath still remains uncut.

One of the intact fibers of the desired size is selected and all the remaining fibers are cut across (5). When necessary, the damaged fibers and the pieces of connective-tissue are removed and cleaned (6 to 8). The preparation can be transferred in a Petri dish by sliding it along the wet surface of the glass plate.

SIMPLEST METHOD OF RECORDING ACTION CURRENTS FROM SINGLE FIBER

The simplest way to record action currents from the single fiber thus isolated and kept in a Petri dish is as follows: immerse a ground electrode in the fluid in the dish, stick the distal end of the preparation to the tip of the grid electrode (e.g., Ag-AgCl) which is held by a movable stand and elevate the distal portion of the preparation into the air step by step until the operated region of the single fiber preparation just reaches the surface of the fluid. Stimulation of the proximal portion of the preparation, also brought above the surface of the fluid and laid on a pair of stimulating electrodes, gives, if the fiber is capable of carrying impulses, invariably a deflection of the cathode ray oscillograph connected to the amplifier. In this case, it is desirable, as is well known, to synchronize application of stimuli to the sweep of the electron beam. If care is taken to pour paraffin oil into the Petri dish and to keep both the grid and stimulating electrodes in the layer of oil, action currents of the fiber can be observed for a day or two.

It should be born in mind in this observation that the voltage developed by the single fiber across the two lead electrodes varies between 0 and about 10 millivolts depending on the input resistance of the amplifier. According to Ohm's law, the maximum voltage observable is given by the product $R \times I$, where R is the (resultant) input resistance of the amplifier and I the maximum value of the current produced by the fiber, which is, in the large motor fiber of the frog, approximately 2×10^{-9} ampere.

In the experiments described in this book, the capacity of the wire leading to the grid of the amplifier is considered to be of the order of 5×10^{-11} farad. To avoid distortion of the observed action current records by this capacity, therefore, care has been taken not to increase the input resistance of the amplifier above 2×10^{5} ohms. The amplifier used was a condenser-coupled one which showed a uniform characteristic for A.C. between 0.05 and 50 kc. per second.

NERVOUS TRANSMISSION AS A MATHEMATICAL PROBLEM

The process of nervous transmission has been treated mathematically by several previous investigators (e.g., Cremer, 1924; Rashevsky, 1931; Rushton, 1937; and others). Although all these theories involve serious errors and limitations, due to oversimplified assumptions as to the structure of the nerve fiber, they have something to their credit. They have not only urged other people to investigate this problem further, but also they predicted the results of some of the experiments which otherwise would have failed to attract the attention of physiologists.

The purpose of this part of the Appendix is to express our idea concerning nervous transmission in mathematical language, making a set of rather crude assumptions. The present author is aware of at least some of the limitations of the present scheme of argument.

Assumption 1: The nerve fiber is represented by an electrical network as shown by the diagram of Figure 77. The capacity of the myelin sheath c is of the order of 10 $\mu\mu$F/cm and the resistance r approximately 100 megohm·cm. The resistance R and the capacity K of the resting node are approximately 2 $\mu\mu$F and 80 megohms respectively (Hodler, Staempfli and Tasaki, 1952). Since the main part of this network consists of physiologically inactive elements, we may neglect the nonlinearity of the network in our consideration of the spreading of currents along the network.

Assumption 2: When the change in the potential difference across a node surpasses a certain critical value V_c an electromotive force E is developed at this node. The time-course of this electromotive force is independent of the applied stimulus.

Assumption 3: The time-interval from the moment at which V_c is attained at a node to the instant when the action-electromotive force reaches the maximum is far shorter than the time-constants of the network of Figure 77. The falling phase of the electromotive force is slow as compared with the time-constants of the network.

These assumptions hold good undoubtedly only at relatively high temperatures at which the development of electromotive force proceeds rapidly as compared to the rate of spread of the potential wave along the network. Based upon these assumptions,

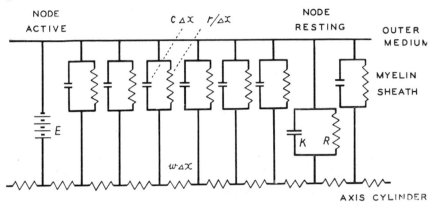

Fig. 77. The electrical network representing the state of the nerve fiber around the active-resting boundary. R, resistance through the plasma membrane of a resting node; K, capacity of a resting node; w, resistance per unit length of the axis-cylinder; x, the distance along the fiber; r, resistance of the myelin sheath of the unit length; c, capacity per unit length of the myelin sheath; E, the electromotive force of the active node. The resistance of the surrounding fluid medium is neglected.

it should be possible to develop a new mathematical theory of nervous transmission. Although the exact explicit expression of the solution of this problem has not been worked out yet, it seems clear that such a theory gives explanations to a number of experimental facts which are often considered to be contradictory to the concept of "saltatory transmission."

The rate of transmission, for example, is determined, when the electromotive force developed is well above the critical voltage V_c, mainly by the capacity of the node and the myelin sheath. This is what Huxley and Stämpfli have answered to the question raised by Sanders and Whitteridge (1946) who found that the internodal distance could differ markedly without being accompanied by an appreciable change in the transmission rate.

Quite recently, Laporte (1950), using nerve fibers innervating the carp lateral line, observed that the start of the action potential, which was recorded from the surface of the nerve bundle, varied continuously as the distance along the nerve fiber. This fact is not at all contradictory to the concept of saltatory transmission, because, in the system which behaves in accordance with the assumption stated above, the potential of the axis-cylinder is given by a continuous function of distance x along the fiber. The potential of the surface of a nerve trunk with uniform thickness is considered to portray the potential of the axis cylinder (see p. 136, Eq. 2).

In the original concept of saltatory transmission suggested by Lillie (1925), the myelin sheath is assumed to be a complete insulator of electricity, nodes of Ranvier being the only places where the energy and time required for transmission are dissipated. The actual myelin sheath, however, shows a very low resistance to a quickly changing current. Some investigators seem to believe that this fact is inconsistent with the concept of saltatory transmission (e.g., Lorente de Nó, 1948). But the present-day concept of saltatory transmission does not include dissipation of transmission-time only at the nodes. It has been stressed, on the contrary, that the utilization-time and the latent period in electrical excitation are mainly, if not exclusively, accounted for by the distributed capacity of the myelin sheath (Tasaki, 1950; Hodler, Stämpfli and Tasaki, 1952). The main point in our conclusion is that the process which occurs in the myelin-covered portion of the nerve fiber is "passive" and "physical" in nature, the "active" physico-chemical processes which make the transmission possible being localized at the nodes.

In their 1949 paper, Huxley and Stämpfli described a series of experiments in support of the concept of saltatory transmission. Among the many experiments they have done, their method of determining the capacity of the myelin sheath is surprisingly beautiful. They described therein the results which seemed to indicate that the time required for transmission is spent mainly at the nodes of Ranvier (*J. Physiol.*, 108:322, Fig. 7). The time intervening between the shock and the peak of the action current was found to increase stepwise as the site of recording the action current crossed a node. From the assumptions mentioned above, however, a marked delay in the time of maximum of the action currents is expected, because the rate of spread of the current along the network of Figure 77 is considered to be limited by the capacity of the myelin sheath. This point, together with other conclusions drawn from the assumptions stated above, was subjected to direct experimental investigation in the University of Bern (Hodler, Staempfli and Tasaki, 1952).

It was revealed by this investigation that (1) the shock-response interval for propagated impulses, (2) the rapidity of the rising phase of the action current, (3) the rapidity of rise of potential in the axis-cylinder, (4) the shape of the strength-latency curve in direct electrical stimulation, and so on, vary considerably within an internode as a function of distance from a node of Ranvier. These results support, at least qualitatively, the validity of our argument stated above.

In nervous transmission at low temperatures and also in direct electrical excitation of a nerve fiber with the electrode placed directly on one of the nodes of Ranvier, however, the third assumption mentioned above is no longer valid. The present author believes now that under such experimental conditions the mathematical treatment of the problem from an entirely different angle, namely, the one based on the consideration of movement of ions across the surface membrane of the nerve fiber (Hodgkin, Huxley and Katz: *Arch. Sc. Physiol.*, 3:129), should give a satisfactory result. As a mathematical problem, analysis of nervous transmission in the myelinated fiber is not a simple one. If we consider both the non-linear ionic current at the node and the complex electrical network of Figure 77 simultaneously, actual solution of the problem seems to be extremely difficult.

It seems worth mentioning briefly the problem of subthreshold response in the myelinated fiber. Consideration of the non-linear ionic current through the nodal membrane provides us with a very satisfactory explanation of the small "response" recorded by Tasaki and Takeuchi (1942) from a node of Ranvier at the site of stimulation. As has been pointed out by British physiologists, the present author's original explanation of this subthreshold response must now be revised.

Katz (1936) explained the non-linearity in the time-course of the threshold change induced by a subthreshold shock and revealed by another shock solely in terms of a local subthreshold response. This explanation, however, should be modified at least partly, because the time-course of the excitatory state has been shown to vary considerably as a function of distance from a node of Ranvier (Tasaki, 1950c). At least a part of this non-linearity should be attributed to the delayed rise of the voltage across the nodal membrane owing to the capacity of the myelin sheath (Tasaki, 1942). In order to treat this problem in a general manner, therefore, we have again to consider the two factors, i.e. the non-linear ionic current through the node of Ranvier and the complex electrical network of Figure 77.

SOME IMPLICATIONS OF THE SALTATORY NATURE OF NERVOUS TRANSMISSION

There has been doubt among histologists about the existence of nodes of Ranvier along the myelinated nerve fibers in the central nervous system. This situation caused scepticism concerning the applicability of the saltatory theory to the fibers in the central nervous system. Quite recently, however, nodes in the spinal cord were re-discovered by Feindel, Allison and Weddell (1948), by Huxley and Staempfli (1949b) and by Hess and Young (1949a). Furthermore, it was shown by Hess and Young (1949b) that there is a linear relationship between the internodal length and the fiber diameter, just as in the peripheral nerve fiber. Although the extreme sensitivity of the spinal cord and the brain to mechanical manipulation is still preventing direct experimental study of the mechanism of transmission in the central nervous system, it seems unlikely that the mechanism in the central nervous system is very different from that in the peripheral nerve fiber.

The following implication of the electrical nature of transmission in the peripheral nerve fiber is very interesting in relation to the sense organs and the central nervous system. Suppose we follow the process of re-stimulation by action current backward along the peripheral nerve fiber, toward the sensory ending in the afferent fiber and centrally in the efferent fiber. We finally come to the point on the fiber at which the sensory stimulus or the central excitatory state is considered to cause an outward-directed current through the surface membrane of the nerve fiber. At this particular point the sensory ending can be regarded simply as a transducer which changes the external sensory stimulus into electrical current and stimulates the initial part of the afferent fiber electrically, and the motoneurone can be considered as a generator of current which induces single or repetitive discharges of impulses in the motor fiber.

It is well known that the discharge of impulses from sensory endings are strongly modified by passage of electric currents through the region of the nerve ending; this fact seems to favor the above-stated view. The strong interaction between sensory and electrical stimuli applied to the Pacinian corpuscle (Gray and Malcolm, 1949) and to the frog's cutaneous ending (Tasaki, unpublished) provides us with stronger evidence in support of this view. Granit's observation on his "generator" potential (1947) and Katz's direct demonstration of a D.C. potential at the frog's muscle spindle give us further support. As Gray and Matthews' study (1951) indicates, the adaptation of the endorgan to sustained sensory stimuli can be considered as a problem dealing with the decay of the generator potential and the accommodation of the sensory nerve fiber to electric currents.

It has been shown by Matthews (1933) and confirmed by Tasaki (1950a) that the rhythm of sensory discharge from the muscle spindle is "reset" by the arrival of an antidromic impulse: the interval between the arrival of an antidromic impulse and the initiation of the next impulse is approximately equal to the usual interval between the orthodromic impulses at that condition. This phenomenon can be regarded as indicating that there is no proper rhythm of activity in the nerve ending itself and the interval between the impulses is determined by the intensity of the continuous "internal" stimulus and the refractory period of the nerve fiber. A similar phenomenon has been observed in the pace-maker of the heart (Gilson, 1936) and also in the pace-maker induced in the peripheral nerve fiber by application of direct current (Tasaki, 1951a). The fact that the rhythm of strychnine potentials in the spinal cord can also be reset by a volley of antidromic impulses (Bremer and Bonnet, 1948) seems to indicate the similarity of the mechanism of repetition in the central nervous system and in the peripheral nerve fiber.

The existence of a "generator" potential in the central nervous system and in the sympathetic ganglion has already been established by Barron and Matthews (1938) and by Eccles (1943). In the neuromuscular transmission, the intervention of one electrical phase, among other chemical series of events, is still better established (Kuffler, 1942 and others). Gesell and his collaborators (1947 and 1949) have collected data in support of his "electrotonic theory of nervous integration" (Gesell, 1940), which primarily intended to interpret the activity of the respiratory center in terms of electrotonic polarization of the cell body. Thus, it seems to the author of this book that experimental evidence of such an electric theory for the sensory nerve endings and for the central nervous system is now gradually accumulating.

REFERENCES

ADRIAN, E. D.: On the conduction of subnormal disturbances in normal nerve. *J. Physiol.*, 45:389–412, 1912.

——: The recovery process of excitable tissues, Part II. *J. Physiol.*, 55:193–225, 1921.

——, and BRONK, D. W.: The discharge of impulses in motor nerve fibres, Part I. Impulses in single fibres of the phrenic nerve. *J. Physiol.*, 66:81–101, 1928.

BARRON, D. H., and MATTHEWS, B. H. C.: The interpretation of potential changes in the spinal cord. *J. Physiol.*, 92:276–321, 1938.

BISHOP, G. H.: The reactance of nerve and the effect upon it of electrical currents. *Am. J. Physiol.*, 89:618–639, 1929.

——: The action potentials at normal and depressed regions of non-myelinated fibers, with special references to "monophasic" lead. *J. Cell. & Comp. Physiol.*, 5:151–169, 1934–35.

——, ERLANGER, J., and GASSER, H. S.: Distortion of action potentials as recorded from the nerve surface. *Am. J. Physiol.*, 78:592–609, 1926.

BISHOP, G. H., and HEINBECKER, P.: Differentiation of axon types in visceral nerves by means of the potential record. *Am. J. Physiol.*, 94:170–200, 1930.

BLAIR, E. A., and ERLANGER, J.: A comparison of the characteristics of axons through their individual electrical responses. *Am. J. Physiol.*, 106:524–564, 1933.

——: Propagation and extention of excitatory effects of the nerve action potential across non-responding internodes. *Am. J. Physiol.*, 126:97–108, 1939.

BOGUE, J. Y., and ROSENBERG, H.: Development and spread of electrotonus. *J. Physiol.*, 82:353–368, 1934.

BRAMWELL, J. C., and LUCAS, KEITH: On the relation of the refractory period to the propagated disturbance in nerve. *J. Physiol.*, 42:495–511, 1911.

BREMER, F., and BONNET, V.: Nouvelles recherches sur le tétanos strychnique de la moelle épinière. *J. de Physiologie*, 40:132A–133A, 1948.

COLE, K. S., and CURTIS, H. J.: Electric impedance of the squid giant axon during activity. *J. Gen. Physiol.*, 22:649–670, 1939.

COLE, K. S., and HODGKIN, A. L.: Membrane and protoplasm resistance in the squid giant axon. *J. Gen. Physiol.*, 22:671–687, 1939.

CREMER, M.: Ueber die Berechnung der Fortpflanzungsgeschwindigkeit im Nerven auf Grund der Stromtheorie der Erregungsleitung. *Beitr. Z. Physiol.*, 2:31–32, 1924.

———: Handbuch der normalen und pathologischen Physiologie. 9:244–284, 1929.

CURTIS, H. J., and COLE, K. S.: Membrane action potentials from the squid giant axon. *J. Cell & Comp. Physiol.*, 15:147–157, 1940.

DAVIS, H., and BRUNSWICK, D.: Studies of the nerve impulse. I. Quantitative method of electrical recording. *Am. J. Physiol.*, 75:497–531, 1926.

DAVIS, H.; FORBES, A.; BRUNSWICK, D., and HOPKINS, A. McH.: Studies of the nerve impulse, II. The question of decrement. *Am. J. Physiol.*, 76:448–471, 1926.

ECCLES, J. C.: Synaptic potentials and transmission in sympathetic ganglion. *J. Physiol.*, 101:465–483, 1943.

ECCLES, J. C., and SHERRINGTON, C. S.: Numbers and contraction values of individual motor-units examined in some muscles of the limb. *Proc. Roy. Soc., London, s.B*, 106:326–357, 1930.

EICHLER, W.: Ueber die Entwicklung der Nervenerregung am Reizorte. *Pflügers Arch. f. d. ges. Physiol.*, 242:468–493, 1939.

ERLANGER, J.: The initiation of impulses in axons. *J. Neurophysiol.*, 2:370–379, 1939.

———, and BLAIR, E. A.: Manifestation of segmentation in myelinated axons. *Am. J. Physiol.*, 110:287–311, 1934.

———: Facilitation and difficilitation effected by nerve impulse in peripheral fibers. *J. Neurophysiol.*, 3:107–127, 1940.

ERLANGER, J., and GASSER, H. S.: The action potential in fibers of slow conduction in spinal roots and somatic nerves. *Am. J. Physiol.*, 92:43–82, 1930.

———: *Electrical Signs of Nervous Activity.* University of Pennsylvania, Philadelphia, 1937.

ERLANGER, J.; GASSER, H. S., and BISHOP, G. H.: The absolutely refractory phase of the alpha, beta and gamma fibers in the sciatic nerve of the frog. *Am. J. Physiol.*, 81:473–474, 1927.

FEINDEL, W. H., ALLISON, A. C., and WEDDELL, G.: Intravenous methylene blue for experimental studies on the central nervous system. *J. Neurol. Neurosurg. Psychiat.*, 11:227–238, 1948.

FULTON, J. F., and NACHMANSOHN, D.: Acetylcholine and the physiology of the nervous system. *Science*, 97:569–571, 1943.

GASSER, H. S., and ERLANGER, J.: The nature of conduction of an impulse in the relatively refractory period. *Am. J. Physiol.*, 73:613–635, 1925.

———: The role played by the sizes of the constituent fibers of a nerve trunk in determining the form of its action potential wave. *Am. J. Physiol.*, 80:522–547, 1927.

GASSER, H. S., and GRUNDFEST, H.: Axon diameters in relation to the spike dimensions and the conduction velocity in mammalian A fibers. *Am. J. Physiol., 127:393–414*, 1939.

GERARD, R. W.: Nerve metabolism. *Physiol. Rev., 12:469–592*, 1932.

GESELL, R.: Neurophysiological interpretation of the respiratory act. *Ergebn. Physiol., 43:477–639*, 1940.

——; HANSEN, E. T., and SISKEL, J.: On the electrotonic nature of stimulation, inhibition, summation and after-discharge of nerve centers. *Am. J. Physiol., 148:515–529*, 1947.

——; HUNTER, J., and LILLIE, R.: Electrical and functional activity of motor neurons. *Am. J. Physiol., 159:15–28*, 1949.

GILSON, A. S.: The effects upon the heart rhythm of premature stimuli applied to the pace-maker and to the atrium. *Am. J. Physiol., 116: 358–366*, 1936.

GRANIT, R.: *Sensory Mechanism of the Retina.* London, 1947.

GRAY, J. A. B., and MALCOLM, J. L.: The initiation of nerve impulses by mesenteric Pacinian corpuscles. *Proc. Roy. Soc. B, 137:96–114,* 1950.

——, and MATTHEWS, P. B. C.: A comparison of the adaptation of the Pacinian corpuscle with the accommodation of its own axon. *J. Physiol., 114:454–464*, 1951.

HERMANN, L.: *Grundrisse der Physiologie.* 323, 1872.

——: Beiträge zur Theorie der Erregungsleitung und der elektrischen Erregung. *Pflügers Arch. f. d. ges. Physiol., 75:574–590*, 1899.

——: Zur Physiologie und Physik des Nerven. *Pflügers Arch. f. d. ges. Physiol., 109:95–144*, 1906.

HESS, A., and YOUNG, J. Z.: Nodes of Ranvier in the central nervous system. *J. Physiol., 108:52 P*, 1949a.

——: Correlation of internodal length and fibre diameter in the central nervous system. *Nature, 164:490–491*, 1949b.

HODGKIN, A. L.: Evidence for electrical transmission in nerve. *J. Physiol., 90:183–210* (Part I) and 211–232 (Part II), 1937.

——: The relation between conduction velocity and the electrical resistance outside a nerve fibre. *J. Physiol., 94:560–570*, 1939.

——: The effect of potassium on the surface membrane of an isolated axon. *J. Physiol., 106:319–340*, 1947.

HODGKIN, A. L., and HUXLEY, A. F.: Action potentials recorded from inside a nerve fibre. *Nature, 144:710–712*, 1939.

——: Resting and action potentials in single nerve fibres. *J. Physiol., 104:176–195*, 1945.

——: Potassium leakage from an active nerve fibre. *J. Physiol., 106: 341–367*, 1947.

HODGKIN, A. L., and RUSHTON, W. A. H.: The electrical constants of a crustacean nerve fibre. *Proc. Roy. Soc., London s.B., 133:444–479,* 1946.

HODLER, J.; STAEMPFLI, R., and TASAKI, I.: The role of the potential wave spreading along the myelinated nerve fiber in excitation and conduction. *Am. J. Physiol., 170*:375–389, 1952.

HURSH, J. B.: Conduction velocity and diameter of nerve fibers. *Am. J. Physiol., 127*:131–139, 1939.

HURUYAMA, M.: The dependence of the extinction-time upon the number of nodes of Ranvier in narcosis of single nerve fibers (Japanese). *Keio Igaku, 21*:201–205, 1941.

HUXLEY, A. F., and STAEMPFLI, R.: Beweiss, der saltatorischen Erregungsleitung im markhaltigen peripheren Nerven. *Helvet. Physiol. Pharmacol. Acta, 6*:C22–25, 1948.

——: Evidence for saltatory conduction in peripheral myelinated nerve fibres. *J. Physiol., 108*:315–339, 1949.

——: Saltatory transmission of the nervous impulse. *Arch. Sc. Physiol., 3*:435–448, 1949.

——: Direkte Bestimmung des Membranpotentials der markhaltigen Nervenfaser in Ruhe und Erregung. *Helvet. Physiol. Pharmacol. Acta, 8*:107–109, 1950.

JEANS, J.: *The Mathematical Theory of Electricity and Magnetism,* 1933.

KATO, G.: *The Theory of Decrementless Conduction in Narcotized Region of Nerve.* Tokyo, Nankodo, 1924.

——: *The Further Studies on Decrementless Conduction.* Tokyo, Nankodo, 1926.

——: *The Microphysiology of Nerve.* Tokyo, Maruzen, 1934.

——: On the excitation, conduction and narcotisation of single nerve fibers. *Cold Spring Harbor Symposia on Quantitative Biology, 4:* 202–213, 1936.

KATZ, B.: *Electric Excitation of Nerve.* London, 1936.

——: Depolarization of sensory terminals and the initiation of impulses in the muscle spindle. *J. Physiol., 111*:261–282, 1950.

KATZ, B., and SCHMITT, O. II.: Electric interaction between two adjacent nerve fibres. *J. Physiol., 97*:471–488, 1940.

KUBO, M.; ONO, S., and TASAKI, I.: In Kato, G., 1934, p. 68–76.

KUBO, M., and YUGE, A.: On the relation between the fiber-diameter and the internodal distance in peripheral nerves. *Collected Papers, A Tribute to Prof. H. Ishikawa,* 1938, p. 114.

KUFFLER, S. W.: Electric potential changes at an isolated nerve-muscle junction. *J. Neurophysiol., 5*:18–26, 1942.

KWASSOW, D. G., and NAUMENKO, A. I.: Störungen in der isolierten Leitung der Impulse im durch hypertonische Lösungen und Austroknung alterierten Nervenstamm. *Pflügers Arch. f. d. ges. Physiol., 237*:576–584, 1936.

LAPORTE, Y.: Conduction continué dans les fibres nerveuses myelinées pheripheriques. *Abstr. XVIIth Internat. Congr.,* 1950, p. 327.

LILLIE, R. S.:   1923 *Protoplasmic Action and Nervous Action*.   Chicago, University of Chicago Press, 1923.
——:   Factors affecting transmission and recovery in the passive iron nerve model.   *J. Gen. Physiol.*, 7:473–507, 1926.
LORENTE DE NÓ, R.:   A *Study of Nerve Physiology*.   New York, 1948.
LUCAS, KEITH: *The Conduction of the Nerve Impulse*.   London, 1917.
MARMONT, G.:   Action potential artefacts from single nerve fibers. *Am. J. Physiol.*, 130:392–402, 1940.
MARRAZZI, A. S., and LORENTE DE NÓ, R.:   Interaction of neighbouring fibers in myelinated nerve.   *J. Neurophysiol.*, 7:83–102, 1944.
MARUYAMA, T.:   Properties of the myelin sheath (Japanese).   *Keio Igaku*, 22: p. 520.
MATTEUCI, C.:   Sur un phénomène physiologique produit par les muscles en contraction.   *C. R. Acad. Sci., Paris*, 4:797–801, 1942.
MATTHEWS, B. H. C.:   Nerve endings in mammalian muscle.   *J. Physiol.*, 78:1–53, 1933.
VON MURALT, A.:   *Die Signaluebermittelung im Nerven*.   Basel, 1945.
OSTERHOUT, W. J. V., and HILL, S. E.:   Salt bridges and negative variations.   *J. Gen. Physiol.*, 13:547–552, 1930.
PFAFFMANN, C.:   Potentials in the isolated medullated axon.   *J. Cell & Comp. Physiol.*, 16:407–410, 1940.
RASHBASS, C., and RUSHTON, W. A. H.:   Space distribution of excitability in the frog's sciatic nerve stimulated by slot electrodes.   *J. Physiol.*, 109:327–342, 1949a.
——:   Space distribution of excitability in the frog's sciatic nerve stimulated by polar electrodes.   *J. Physiol.*, 109:343–353, 1949b.
RASHEVSKY, N.:   On the theory of nervous conduction.   *J. Gen. Physiol.*, 14:517–528, 1931.
——:   *Mathematical Biophysics*.   Chicago, University of Chicago Press, 1938, chaps. XIX and XX.
DE RENYI, G. ST.:   The structure of cells in tissues as revealed by microdissection, II.   *J. Comp. Neurol.*, 47:405–425, 1928–29.
RICHARD, C. H., and GASSER, H. S.:   After-potentials and recovery curve of C fibers.   *Am. J. Physiol.*, 113:108–109, 1935.
ROSENBLUETH, A.:   The stimulation of myelinated axons by nerve impulses in adjacent myelinated axons.   *Am. J. Physiol.*, 132:119–128, 1941.
RUSHTON, W. A. H.:   Nerve excitation by multipolar electrodes.   *J. Physiol.*, 66:217–230, 1928.
——:   Initiation of the propagated disturbance.   *Proc. Roy. Soc., London, s.B.*, 124:210–243, 1937.
SANDERS, F. K., and WHITTERIDGE, D.:   Conduction velocity and myelin thickness in regenerating nerve fibres.   *J. Physiol.*, 105:152–174, 1946.
SCHAEFER, H., and SCHMITZ, W.:   Aktionsstrom und Hüllenleitfähigkeit.   *Pflüger's Arch. f. d. ges. Physiol.*, 234:737–747, 1934.

SCHMITZ, W., and SCHAEFER, H.: Ladekurve, Ladezeit und Latenz-zeit der Aktion bei elektrischer Nervenreizung. *Pflügers Arch. f. d. ges. Physiol.,* 233:229–247, 1934.

STAEMPFLI, R.: Untersuchungen an der einzolnen, lebenden Nerven-faser des Frosches. *Helv. Physiol. Pharmacol. Acta,* 4:411–415 (1. Mitteilung) und 417–422 (2. Mitteilung), 1946.

TASAKI, I.: The strength-duration relation of the normal, polarized and narcotized nerve fiber. *Am. J. Physiol.,* 125:367–379, 1939a.

——: Electrical stimulation and the excitatory process in the nerve fiber. *Am. J. Physiol.,* 125:380–395, 1939b.

——: The electro-saltatory transmission of the nerve impulse and the effect of narcosis upon the nerve fiber. *Am. J. Physiol.,* 127:211–227, 1939c.

——: Mikrophysiologische Untersuchungen über die Grundlage der Erregungsleitung in der markhaltigen Nervenfaser. *Pflügers Arch. f. d. ges. Physiol.,* 244:125–141, 1940.

——: Das Schwellenabsinken bei Reizung einer Nervenfaser mit kurzen Strömstössen. *Pflügers Arch. f. d. ges. Physiol.,* 245:665–679, 1942.

——: *The Physiology of the Nerve Fiber* (Japanese). Tokyo, 1944.

——: The excitatory and recovery processes in the nerve fibre as modified by temperature changes. *Biochem. Biophys. Acta,* 3:498–509, 1949.

——: The threshold conditions in electrical excitation of the nerve fiber, Part I and II. *Cytologia,* 15:205–236, 1950a.

——: Excitation of a single nerve fiber by the action current from another single fiber. *J. Neurophysiol.,* 13:177–183, 1950b.

——: Nature of the local excitatory state in the nerve fiber. *Jap. J. Physiol.,* 1:75–85, 1950c.

TASAKI, I., and FUJITA, M.: Action currents of single nerve fibers as modified by temperature changes. *J. Neurophysiol.,* 11:311–315, 1948.

TASAKI, I.; ISHII, K., and ITO, H.: On the relation between the con-duction-rate, the fiber-diameter and the internodal distance of the medullated nerve fiber. *Jap. J. M. Sc., III Biophysics,* 9:189–199, 1943.

TASAKI, I., and MIZUGUCHI, K.: Response of single Ranvier nodes to electrical stimuli. *J. Neurophysiol.,* 11:295–303, 1948.

——: The changes in the electric impedance during activity and the effect of alkaloids and polarization upon the bioelectric processes in the myelinated nerve fiber. *Biochim. Biophys. Acta,* 3:484–493, 1949.

TASAKI, I.; MIZUGUCHI, K., and TASAKI, K.: Modification of the elec-tric response of a single Ranvier node by narcosis, refractoriness and polarization. *J. Neurophysiol.,* 11:305–310, 1948.

TASAKI, I., and TASAKI, N.: The electrical field which a transmitting

nerve fiber produces in the fluid medium. *Biochim. Biophys. Acta,*
5:335–342, 1950.

TASAKI, I., and TAKEUCHI, T.:   1941 Der am Ranvierschen Knoten
entstehende Aktionsstrom und seine Bedeutung für die Erregungsleitung. *Pflügers Arch. f. d. ges. Physiol., 244:696–711,* 1941.

———: Weitere Studien über den Aktionsstrom der markhaltigen
Nervenfaser und über die elektrosaltatorische Übertragung des
Nervenimpulses. *Pflügers Arch. f. d. ges. Physiol., 245:764–782,*
1942.

TASAKI, I., and USHIYAMA, J.:   The effect of saponine and several other
chemicals upon the configuration of the action current led through
the myelin sheath. *Arch. Intern. Stud. Neurol., 2:3,* 1950.

TASAKI, I.; YUASA, K., and MORII, I.:   On the mechanism of suspension
of nervous transmission by narcosis. *Jap. J. M. Sc., III Biophysics,*
9:183–188, 1943.

TAKEUCHI, T., and TASAKI, I.:   Uebertragung des Nervenimpulses in
der polarisierten Nervenfaser. *Pflügers Arch. f. d. ges. Physiol.,*
246:32–43, 1942.

TSUKAGOSHI, M.:   A note on the suspension of the nervous transmission
by narcosis (Japanese). *J. Physiol. Soc. Japan, 9:592,* 1944.

WORONZOW, D. S.:   Ueber die Einwirkung des konstanten Stromes auf
den mit Wasser, Zuckerlösung, Alkali- und Erdalkalichloridlösungen
behandelten Nerven. *Pflügers Arch. f. d. ges. Physiol., 203:300–318,*
1924.

ZOTTERMAN, Y.:   A note on the relation between the conduction rate
and fiber size in mammalian nerves. *Skandinav. Arch. f. Physiol.,*
77:123–128, 1937.

INDEX

In this index the words which appear in many other articles but have not been used in the text (e.g. unmedullated fiber instead of non-myelinated fiber) are also included to show the equivalent words in this book.

A

absolutely refractory period, 82, 88, 104, 105, 125
action current
  from a single fiber, 10
  from a single node of Ranvier, 16–19, 80–82, 90–93, 107–108
action-e.m.f., 33, 52–53, 57, 125
action potential
  in conducting medium, 60–66
  diphasic, 134–138
  monophasic, 129–133
  of a single fiber, 11, 127
Adrian, E. D., 5, 88, 101, 102, 141
Adrian's law, 88
Allison, A. C., 151
all-or-none, 81, 84, 91, 97, 104
anelectrotonus, 107–120
attenuation constant, 28, 31

B

Barron, D. H., 152
binodal action current, 39
Bishop, G. H., 51, 121, 125, 126, 138
Blair, E. A., 113, 116, 117, 121
block of transmission
  by electrotonus, 108–115
  at internode, 78–79
  by narcosis, 96–102
  in refractory period, 95–106
Bogue, J. Y., 69
Bonnet, V., 152
Bramwell, J. G., 96
break excitation, 74
Bremer, F., 152
bridge-insulator, 12
Bronk, D. W., 5, 141
brucine, 89
Brunswick, D., 101, 138

C

CaCl₂—effect upon myelin sheath, 76
capacity of myelin sheath, 69, 146
catelectrotonus, 107–120
cathodal depression, 113
cocaine—effect upon
  myelin sheath, 75
  nerve trunk, 99
  node of Ranvier, 90–93
Cole, K. S., 31, 32, 54, 138, 139, 140
conduction block (see block of transmission)
conduction velocity (see rate of transmission)
Cremer, M., 38, 146
critical concentration of narcotic, 98–99, 102
critical (slowest) rate of transmission, 98
Curtis, H. J., 31, 32, 54, 138, 139

D

Davis, H., 101, 138
decrement of impulse, 102
depolarization, 52
diphasic action potential, 134–138
duration of spike, 19, 65, 88, 125

E

Eccles, J. C., 137, 152
Eichler, W., 51
electric field produced by a fiber, 60
electrolyte—effect upon myelin sheath, 76
electrotonus, 107–120
emetine, 89
Erlanger, J., 87, 113, 116, 117, 121, 125, 126, 131, 133, 138
ethanol, 91